AMERICA CAN COMPETE

By:

James Gooch
Program Manager
Manufacturing Technical Education
International Business Machines Corp.
Austin, Texas

Michael L. George
Director
Institute of Business Technology
Dallas, Texas

Douglas C. Montgomery
John M. Fluke Distinguished Professor of
Manufacturing Engineering
University of Washington
Seattle, Washington

Additional Copies may be obtained from:
The Institute of Business Technology
13355 Noel Rd. Suite 800, Dallas, TX 75240
(214) 661-8066

PURPOSE OF THE WORK

The purpose of this work is to provide executives and engineers with the course of action which must be taken to manufacture the highest quality, lowest cost products worldwide thus proving "America Can Compete."

Dedicated To

the memory of

THOMAS J. WATSON, SR.

who was committed to the dignity of the individual, integrity in dealing with customers, and the application of the Golden Rule in business. His example of courage in adversity is a continual challenge to the best within us, and an inspiration to those who strive to achieve important goals.

ACKNOWLEDGEMENT

The authors wish to thank William P. Clements, Jr., Governor of Texas, for his encouragement of this work, and for the time and energy he has devoted to excellence in engineering education.

TABLE OF CONTENTS

Page

INTRODUCTION   America Can Compete   5

CHAPTER 1   The American Manufacturing Revolution   11

CHAPTER 2   The Marketing Era in America   23

CHAPTER 3   The Wasteful Factory   28

CHAPTER 4   The *New* Manufacturing Revolution   39

CHAPTER 5   Product Flexibility with Low Cost   64

CHAPTER 6   Quality with Low Cost   73

CHAPTER 7   Prevention of Defects   81

CHAPTER 8   Robotics, Automation and CIM   94

CHAPTER 9   Developing the Corporate Strategy   108

CHAPTER 10   Continuous Flow Manufacturing at IBM   125

CHAPTER 11   People Involvement   154

APPENDIX I   Rapid Setup   157

APPENDIX II   Statistical Process Control   169

GLOSSARY

INDEX

AMERICA CAN COMPETE

Introduction

American manufacturers have an unprecedented opportunity to restore competitiveness to the birthplace of mass production. A new manufacturing method has recently been developed which is superior to the Japanese method. Over the past fifteen years the Japanese have taken major shares of American markets including semiconductors, automobiles, steel, video cassette recorders, television, etc. It has been estimated that two million jobs have been lost to imports. The recent (1987) strengthening of the Yen has forced the Japanese to raise prices, temporarily halting the onslaught. American manufacturers must seize this opportunity to apply this new manufacturing method to restore the balance of competitive strength. Manufacturers who do not now face Japanese competition should apply these new methods to improve quality and profitability.

The reasons for the lower prices and higher quality of Japanese products is often misunderstood. Many believe that the Japanese advantage is due to cultural differences (the Samurai theory). Yet the most efficient Sony and Nissan plants are in the USA. Others believe that the Japanese "dump" products below cost. The strong financial condition of Japanese companies, their banks, and the strength of the Yen destroy this comfortable theory. Still others believe that the Japanese secret is robotics. However, the world's most efficient engine plant, Toyota's Kamigo No. 9, has no robots. It is three times as productive as a comparable U.S. factory that is equipped with robots.

Then what is the source of Japanese strength? Informed observers are in agreement that the only thing that all of their successes have in common is the Just In Time manufacturing system.

The other important factor in the Japanese success has been the active involvement of their top management in demanding that the goal of lowest cost, highest quality manufacturing be achieved.

The Just In Time system achieves its success by eliminating the

5

hidden waste of production in large batches. JIT is often mistakenly thought to be an "inventory reduction program." Actually, JIT is a program to reduce cost by 20-30%. Inventory reduction is merely a side benefit of the total cost reduction, quality improvement program.

The problem with JIT is that it is a difficult system to implement. It took Toyota 20 years to implement the system. American manufacturers do not have twenty years to achieve competitiveness. Many U.S. manufacturers have succeeded in implementing JIT in a few divisions, but have not significantly affected corporatewide profitability.

Americas Opportunity: Continuous Flow Manufacturing
A Step Ahead of JIT

A few years ago, IBM set the goal of becoming the lowest cost, highest quality manufacturer in their worldwide markets. As you will learn in Chapter 10, they experienced difficulty with their first implementation of Just In Time. IBM then developed the Continuous Flow Manufacturing method which is a step ahead of Just In Time. Continuous Flow Manufacturing (CFM) incorporates all the benefits of Just In Time, but has the following advantages:

- *Cost reductions and quality improvements are achieved in months, rather than the years.*
- *The CFM method applies to all manufacturing, both high and low volume. JIT applies only to high volume.*
- *Greater cost reductions are possible with CFM.*

Continuous Flow Manufacturing achieves these advantages over JIT because it guides the improvement effort by the use of Line Analysis programs. These easy to learn programs replace the "trial and error" methods of JIT. Line Analysis is fully explained in Chapter 4.

The first application of Continuous Flow Manufacturing at three IBM demonstration plants yielded amazing cost and cycle time reductions, quality improvements, and increased employee enthusiasm.

This book provides a complete description of the implementation of Continuous Flow Manufacturing. Of equal importance, it also defines the essential role that the CEO, Marketing and R&D executives must play in achieving the goal of the lowest cost, highest quality products worldwide. No previous knowledge of manufacturing is needed to understand and apply the methods of this book. The first three chapters develop the necessary background information.

Accepting the Challenge

Some people think that the goal of lowest cost, highest quality production can be achieved by means other than CFM/JIT. As is true of any program requiring change, the biggest problem is in persuading people that the change is both necessary and good, and in obtaining their involvement.

The undeniable cost and quality advantages of JIT and CFM prove that Batch production is uncompetitive and obsolete. However, most manufacturing executives have grown up with Batch production. As you will read in Chapter 10, some IBM managers' response to CFM was, "It's a good system, but it doesn't apply to our business." This was one of the reasons why IBM established CFM demonstrations in three entirely different plants to prove that CFM applied to all manufacturing. All IBM divisions have now accepted the objective of replacing the old Batch production methods with CFM.

Some believe that the Japanese advantages are due solely to quality. These companies have attempted to simply improve the quality of their present Batch production, avoiding change.

In fact, the higher quality of Japanese products is the result of their JIT manufacturing system: economically producing in ever smaller batches, and continually improving the quality of each batch. The continual improvement is due to specific Defect Prevention methods (Chapter 6). Lowest cost, highest quality production thus requires JIT/CFM.

Others believe that a computer scheduling program alone, such as MRP II, provides the means of attaining the lowest cost, highest quality production. MRP II creates workorders for the workcenters based on firm and speculative orders. MRP II effectively increases batch sizes, which as we shall see, runs counter to the methods of JIT/CFM. Lowest cost, highest quality production can only be achieved by the elimination of waste and the prevention of defects at the workcenters. This goal is achieved by specific improvement methods such as Rapid Setup, Operation Improvement, etc., which are the subjects of Chapter 5. MRP II does not even address the need for improvement at the workcenters. If waste is not eliminated at the workcenters, it is impossible to attain the lowest cost and highest quality.

Finally, top management's understanding and support of CFM is essential to success. IBM was fortunate in that the drive to become the lowest cost, highest quality producer came from the top. Top management involvement is essential in assuring that Marketing and R&D understand the goals of the effort and the support they must provide.

The Role of Marketing and R&D

The lowest cost, highest quality manufacturing cannot be achieved without a cooperative effort between Marketing, R&D and Manufacturing.

What is the role of Marketing? Marketing must determine the competitive pricing, features and delivery that is causing orders to be lost. They must seek out new product opportunities, and new markets. What additional sales could be won with lower priced products? Continuous Flow manufacturing is able to yield lower costs, faster delivery times, with a broader product line than is possible with Batch production.

What is the role of R&D? CFM is a more flexible system than Batch production and therefore adapts better to rapid technological change. R&D is thus encouraged to explore new processes and technologies to keep the company's products at the forefront in quality and low cost. R&D and engineering must also cooperate to a higher degree with manufacturing in developing products and processes that conform to the needs of low cost, high quality production. Specific examples and recommendations for the form of this cooperation are described in Chapter 9.

America Can Compete

Some writers have questioned whether American chief executives are able to oversee the implementation of a new manufacturing system.[1] The argument is that, to a large degree, American chief executives have a legal, financial, or marketing background and are not capable of properly implementing a manufacturing solution.

The lack of manufacturing background is no impediment. As you will read in Chapter 1, the founder of the science of manufacturing engineering once wrote:

Good manners, education, special training and skill count for less in an executive position than grit, determination and bulldog endurance that knows no defeat.

Executives must have the grit, determination and bulldog endurance to meet and overcome opposition to the implementation of CFM. If there is any cultural advantage possessed by the Japanese, it lies in this area. Managers with a legal, financial, and marketing background have just as much grit as manufacturing managers. All that is needed is manufacturing literacy. The first three chapters of this book provide all the technical and historical background necessary for an adequate understanding of manufacturing.

Most of the readers of this book will not be CEO's. As managers and engineers you will find that your involvement in the implementation of CFM will be one of the most interesting and rewarding efforts of your career.

America's competitiveness is of international importance. An underproductive America can neither provide a decent living for its people nor maintain the shield under which the Free World dwells in safety.

The authors are convinced that the desire, the will and the ability to again make America the supreme manufacturing nation exists. We believe that Continuous Flow Manufacturing provides the means of fulfilling this important goal.

Good luck and Godspeed in your endeavors!

---

[1]National Academy of Engineering. "Education for the Manufacturing World of the Future". Washington, D.C.: National Academy Press, 1985, pg 29.

CHAPTER 1

The American Manufacturing Revolution

America was still a largely agrarian society in the late 19th century. Britain dominated manufacturing and world trade. The methods of manufacturing "organization" had changed very little since the beginning of the Industrial Revolution. Few would have believed that a manufacturing revolution was in the making. Fewer still could have conceived that it would be born and developed in America, rather than Europe.

At the close of the Nineteenth Century, Industry was still organized around the apprentice-craft system, in which the worker learned his "trade" and supplied his own tools. The emergence of the Factory System did not automatically eliminate the "trades." *The method of getting the job done was primarily left up to the initiative of the worker.* The foreman, representing management, was responsible for preventing idleness and for "driving" the men.

This system led to antagonism between labor and management, with the latter often asserting that workers were "soldiering," i.e., deliberately working slowly. Labor strife at the turn of the Century was intense. The antagonism between labor and management led to many serious strikes, loss of Gross National Product, and much misery.

Frederick Taylor

Frederick W. Taylor (1856-1914), son of a prominent Philadelphia family, took an intense interest in the labor problem in general and in raising productivity in particular. Taylor came to the conclusion that a new approach, which he called "Scientific Management" was needed. The essential tenet of Scientific Management is that: *"Management is responsible for designing and developing the methods by which work is done; it must not be left up to the skill and initiative of the worker."* Only by this means, Taylor believed, could a company create adequate wealth to satisfy both the owners and the workers.

The idea that management should be responsible for developing work methods and furnishing efficient tools was considered novel at that time. The early applications of Taylor's methods were so successful that they inspired a generation of American, and more recently, a generation of Japanese manufacturing engineers.

Taylor's first job was as a machinist at the Midvale Steel Co. He became convinced that most labor and much material is wasted. Following his early experiences at Midvale, he published some note-worthy papers, and set up a business as a consultant.

One of Taylor's earliest jobs as a consultant was at Bethlehem Steel. At Bethlehem, there were about 600 shovelers, and yard laborers. Each man supplied his own shovel, and shoveled various loads, from heavy iron ore to light ash. A typical shovel of iron ore weighed 30 pounds and quickly tired the worker. A shovel load of ash weighed 4 pounds, and the worker was all motion, with little result.

Taylor conducted experiments in which he found that a 21 pound load was most comfortable for the man, and gave the greatest output per day. Taylor then designed 10 different shovels. The smallest would carry a 21 pound load of iron ore; the largest 21 pounds of ash, etc. In addition, he carefully selected and trained the men, and developed a system to schedule their labor. By these means, the work of 600 men was performed by 140. The average tons moved per day per man rose from 16 to 59. The men were paid a bonus, increasing their wages 60%. The cost of moving material fell 50%, including the cost of the bonus. Job analysis, special tools and worker scheduling were the keys to this early experiment.

Another example of the application of Taylor's methods involved bricklaying. In the 19th Century, most large buildings were still made of bricks. Thus bricklaying on a large scale was vastly more important than it is today. One of Taylor's contemporaries, Frank Gilbreath, applied Scientific Management principles to this problem. After 5000 years, and millions of men working the trade, it would seem that no significant improvement could be made in laying bricks. In traditional bricklaying, the worker stooped over and picked up a brick from the heap. He then took several scoops off the mortar board, and layed the brick. He then tapped the brick to obtain a uniform joint thickness.

Gilbreath analyzed the job, broke it down into four elements, and developed special methods to best perform each task.

The bricks were prepared by laying them on a screw table best side up. The worker was also on a screw table with his mortar. The brick table was continually raised to the workers shoulder height, avoiding the bending motion. As the wall went higher, the bricklayer was raised. A special deep mortar box and trowel were devised to require only a single scoop. The mortar consistency was adjusted to eliminate the need for "tapping" the brick.

The result of all these obvious improvements in work methods was that the worker could now lay 350 bricks per man day compared to 120 previously. Further, the quality was improved. The best edge of the brick was always exposed. Bad bricks were never used. Joint thickness was far more uniform due to the ease of the job. Management had again played its role in designing an improved method for getting the work done.

Taylor also worked on the old problem of determining the proper "Feed and Speed" in machining metal. To machine metal in the fastest time, at what rate should you feed the metal to the cutting edge, and how fast should the machine rotate the metal?

Taylor found that the answer depended on the metal's hardness, chemical composition, shaving thickness; a total of twelve simultaneous equations. He developed a slide rule to solve these equations, and published the results in machinist tables. This effort took 26 years of dedicated effort, and gives some insight into his endurance and grit.

Taylor once said:

good manners, education, special training and skill count for less in an executive position than grit, determination and bull dog endurance that knows no defeat.[1]

Taylor and Gilbreath's efforts led to the development of "Time and Motion Study," and to a recognition that management had a great responsibility in designing *how* the work was to be accomplished.

In 1909 Taylor lectured in Detroit, addressing more than 600 superintendents and foremen from all over the city. He was surprised to find that several manufacturers including the Ford Motor Company were already using his principles and methods.[2]

Taylor left behind a large group of dedicated disciples, several notable successes, and a philosophy capable of extension and application. The optimistic outlook that all work methods are susceptible to analysis, subdivision, and improvement, and that we are master of production cost and hence our fate, is largely due to Taylor. Taylor's methods are sometimes criticized because subdivision and specialization may lead to compartmentalization. We shall see how Continuous Flow Manufacturing solves this problem by encouraging operators and engineers to learn a variety of tasks. Nevertheless, Taylor is regarded as the founder of the modern profession of Manufacturing Engineering. His legacy was perpetuated by Colleges and Universities as they developed Industrial and Manufacturing Engineering degree programs.

Henry Ford

The early Ford's, like most other cars, were beautiful but expensive. For example, the biggest seller in 1908 was the luxurious Buick! President Woodrow Wilson decried cars saying, "Nothing so spreads socialism as automobiles," because they were symbols of class distinctions.

Here the attitudes of a Republic founded on equality may have been the deciding factor. We know of Ford's intense interest in and sympathy for the common man. In any event, despite internal opposition from his Board of Directors, Ford decided to build a low cost, durable car to reach a previously untapped market. By 1921, Ford controlled 60% of the U.S. market. This is not the place to tell an oft-told story. What concerns us here is that this titanic achievement was a direct application of Taylor's principles on a massive scale.

One example that Ford was fond of citing was the labor cost reduction of the Magneto Ignition System.[3] This ignition system was used prior to the battery ignition systems. The Magneto Ignition assembly line was one of the first, and certainly most important. Continuous Flow assembly lines in history.

14

Flywheel Magneto Line after improvement

The assembly of the Magneto Ignition system required 29 separate operations. Initially, one man was issued a bag of parts and performed all the operations. The best man could assemble a system in about 20 minutes, although the quality of the job was often unsatisfactory. Parts were sometimes left out, or not tightened enough. This defect was very serious, as the flywheel magneto was bolted to the engine. Magneto defects resulted in failure to start and caused a massive rework problem. About this time, Ford visited a meat packing house and saw sides of beef being transported, with each worker doing only one job. He reasoned that the solution to his magneto problem lay in this example.

The "obvious" step in analysis was to sub-divide or break down the job into 29 separate operations. A production line of 29 men was formed with each man doing one operation, then handing the assembly to the next worker. Each worker checked the one operation done by the previous worker before he did his own job. Any defective work was handed back to the previous worker. This is a technique known as Successive Checks. When assembly line was turned on, the assembly time was reduced to an equivalent of 13 minutes per system. By improving the work method at each operation, and making the time used at each operation equal (balancing the line) the time was reduced to 5 minutes per system. Most importantly, defects were eliminated by Successive Checks with no in process inspection.

The success of this small beginning gave Ford the confidence to proceed to assembling complete motors on Continuous Flow lines, with similar cost reductions. Ultimately, he demanded its use in every facet of production.

It should not be assumed that only complex tasks are capable of important cost reductions and quality improvements. As an example, attaching a piston to a connecting rod is a simple six step operation, and would not seem a good candidate for improvement. The job took an average of 3 minutes, and was considered too simple to need inspection. When rejections from the motor assembly line began to mount, action was needed. To replace a defective piston in a complete engine results in catastrophic rework costs. To improve quality and reduce cost, the job was analyzed using Taylor's methods. It was found that, during a 9 hour day, each assembler spent 4 hours walking!

The job of Piston Assembly was broken down into a 3 man operation with a 4th man as inspector. Each man would perform two operations, then place his completed work on a gravity slide which would pass it to the next man. Assembly time was cut from 185 seconds to 77 seconds, and rejections were eliminated. Fourteen men did more work and a better job than did 28. As the foreman said, *"We were asleep over that job, asleep and dreaming. I don't see how we came to overlook the possibilities we did."*[4]

Rather than ship a completed batch of Piston Assemblies to a quality control station remote from the assembly bench, the fourth man on the bench was an inspector. He was equipped with a steel plate to gauge the pistons, and a Mistake Proof jig to determine if the connection rod was pinched. If it was mis-assembled, the assembly was immediately handed back to the worker to fix (immediate feedback).

As we shall see later, most of the Japanese quality method is contained in this simple example:

1. *Inspection of the product at the* source. *Inspection one-at-a-time, as they are built, preventing accumulation of a bad batch.*
2. *100% inspection.*
3. *Use of Mistake Proof Jigs and Assembly Methods to prevent defects.*
4. *Immediate feedback to workers on defects.*

Effectively, the total quality effort was aimed at prevention of defects at the source. This eliminated rework, scrap, lost capacity and minimized testing. When you cranked a Ford for the first time, it started and ran!

In 1921, the reliability and quality of Ford was praised by Alfred Sloan, the President of General Motors; *"Chevrolet at that time being competitive with Ford neither in price nor quality."*[5] One of the hallmarks of Ford was that there would be a constant increase of Quality, not just an acceptable level.[6]

An army of 300 Manufacturing Engineers at Ford assaulted every phase of assembly and material procurement with the goal of driving down costs to allow reduced sales prices and market expansion. The history of price, sales and profit is instructive:

Year	Unit Sales Price of Model T Runabout	Ford Motor Sales (millions)	Net Income (millions)
1908	$850	$ 4.7	$ 1.1
1909	750	9.0	3.0
1910	680	16.7	4.1
1911	590	24.6	7.8
1912	525	42.5	13.5
1913	500	89.1	27.1
1914	440	119.4	33.0
1915	390	121.1	30.0
1916	345	206.8	57.0

Notice how market demand was stimulated by lowering the price, and how increasing volume led to lower costs and higher profits. At a price of $850, volume only amounted to $4.7 million. At a price of $345, volume soared to $206.8 million.

The material content of the Ford did not vary significantly during this period. The percent profit on sales remained fairly constant despite a 60% reduction in selling price! The 60% reduction was achieved by the elimination of waste due to the transition to Continuous Flow Manufacturing.

One measure of waste is the inventory turns. Inventory turns is defined as Cost of Goods Sold divided by average inventory. A company with high inventory turns has eliminated most of the cost associated with managing inventory, rework, scrap and warranty cost. Ford had slightly more than 3 days inventory, leading to over 80 turns per year. By contrast, most U.S. firms turn inventory in the range of three to six times per year. The lower the inventory turns, the greater is the opportunity for profit improvement.

Let's explore the relationship between waste and inventory turns more fully. Ford was able to transform iron ore to an automobile in 52 hours. Let us assume, that, out of the thousands of possible defects, each Model T had only two defects. To use our examples, we will assume that the fly-wheel magneto, and a piston-connecting rod were defective. When the engine was cranked, it would not start. The complete car would have to be dragged aside, and the cause tracked back to the flywheel magneto. The flywheel is buried in the engine, requiring much time to get it out. It must then be repaired, re-installed. When we again crank the engine, we may notice excessive engine vibration due to the piston defect. We must then tear the engine down and repair it again. The clock is running, and this scenario might take two days, doubling the time the full cost of the car is in inventory. This effectively cuts inventory turns in half for that unit.

What if we didn't notice the engine vibration? The car would then fail in the hands of the customer, with even greater cost!

A company cannot achieve rapid inventory turns if it generates defects. American car manufacturers turn inventory 10 to 15 times per year. Toyota turns inventory 70 times per year. Have you heard of any Toyota recalls? Let us point out that U.S. automobile manufacturers have made tremendous progress in the last five years, but they would agree that much remains to be done.

The Ford System of Continuous Flow production achieved spectacular reductions in cost and improvements in quality. Each sub-assembly line contains all the Operations including machines, processes and assembly stations, needed to complete the sub-assembly. Thus, the production of any part might first require milling, then boring, then grinding. Ford would position these machines in that sequence within arms length of each other, with finished products handed to the next stage. The alternative approach is to position all the metal cutting machines of a given type together. This results in large batches and much hidden waste cost, which will be studied in Chapter 3. Ford even put the Brazing Furnaces in the flow line on the shop floor! Furnaces are normally *"relegated to a separate and despised quarter, far out of the natural line of component travel."*[7] He went to all lengths to maintain continuous flow of product and avoid batch production.

By positioning men and machines in a continuous Flow line, all material flows in one direction. It can be likened to the flow of rivers which feed the Mississippi. Just as no water "builds" up in a river, no inventory built up in the Ford continuous production line. By eliminating any work-in-process inventory build-up; plant size, capital, and inventory investment was drastically reduced. Material flowed from Receiving through to Manufacturing. There was no stockroom; hence no counting, storing, issuing and re-transporting of material took place. We earlier spoke of the results of defect prevention at the source to avoid the waste due to scrap, rework, and lost productivity. Together, these waste elimination efforts resulted in a factory system in which virtually all labor expended adds value to the product. In the book, "Ford Methods and Ford Shops," written in 1913 we read:

> *Every square foot of every workshop carried a certain and inevitable overhead charge, and is hence a debtor to the plant. The only possible way in which any square foot of any factory can be made to pay its existing debt to the plant at large, is to make this square foot of space support a profit earning load.*[8]

All activities which did not add value were eliminated. Examples of non-value added activities include counting, storing, issuing and moving of inventory. As we shall see in Chapter 3, these non-value add efforts rise linearly with inventory, i.e., there is no economy of scale in overhead. The higher the inventory, the higher will be the associated non-value add cost. Thus again, Inventory Turns is a key measure of waste in a system.

By flowing components to their "need" point, assemblies traveled far less distance to be completed. For example, engine blocks had traveled a total of 4000 feet at the Piquette Plant under the old Batch system, and now traveled only 334 feet. The density of machines reached unprecedented levels, allowing workers to pass parts and help one another. The process time from iron ore (Ford made his own steel at the Rouge) to a finished Model T was less than 3 days! It took 50 years before this record was challenged, this time by the Toyota Just In Time production system.

What was the weakness in the Ford Production system? What caused its setback at the hands of General Motors? Ford was famous for the remark "Henry will give you any color you want, so long as it's black." The production machines were setup for one-and-only-one product. The advantage to eliminating any product diversity was that you avoid the need to interrupt production to change tooling setup. Consider an 800 ton press. To change from one die to another typically takes four hours. Thus, if one has two types of doors, one must maintain an inventory of four hours of type A plus the run time on type B plus the re-setup time to get back to type A. With production rates of 3000 cars per day, you must have an inventory of nearly

6000 doors to last until the next run of type A. The alternative is to have a separate press for each product. This involves, instead of inventory investment, a huge capital investment. When a Detroit journalist wrote that the Ford production machines were so cleverly designed that they could switch from car to tractor production instantly, Ford was amused at the man's "ignorance."

Ford's solution was to avoid the dilemma by refusing to allow any variety in product. This avoided the necessity of ever re-setting up a machine or operation. But by allowing no variety in product, he left himself open to destruction by a new strategy. As late as 1924, he still opposed any change to the Model T.

We will close the discussion of the Ford system by pointing out that he anticipated modern manufacturing in every respect but one: Rapid change of set up. Changing the die in a large press was chosen for discussion because it requires one of the longest setup times. What if the setup time could be reduced from 4 hours to 4 minutes? Most of the objection to product variety would evaporate. What is Ford's Legacy? In 1982, Phillip Caldwell, then President of Ford visited Toyota. He inquired as to the secret of Toyota's success. The President of Toyota responded

There is no secret as to how we learned to do what we do Mr. Caldwell, WE LEARNED IT AT THE ROUGE[9]

Ford workers in 1914 earned the industry norm, about $2.67 per nine hour day. In 1914 Ford announced that he would pay a minimum of $5 per day and reduce the workday to 8 hours. "This is neither charity, nor wages, but profit sharing and Efficiency Engineering," said Ford.

Winston Churchill visited America in the 1920's and observed:

Never before had such immense quantities of goods of all kinds been produced, shared, and exchanged in any society. There is, in fact, no limit to the benefit which human beings may bestow upon one another by the highest exertion of their diligence and skill.

Increased sales and profits for the company, lower priced high quality products for the customer and higher wages for the worker show the benefits of the "Highest Exertion of Diligence and Skill." It was true then, it is true now. Ford has been credited by some as being the inventor of the modern age, spreading wealth and convenience to the common man.

Summary

We have discussed Frederick Taylor's principle that "Management must be responsible for the method by which work is done." The application of this principle by Ford led to the creation of high quality low priced goods on a scale with no previous historical parallel. Ford's method allowed a 60% price reduction by the prevention of all defects and the elimination of all non-value add activities. The related measure of how well these waste functions have been eliminated is obtained by calculating the inventory turns ratio. The higher the Inventory Turns, the less waste. The lower the Inventory Turns, the greater the opportunity for profit improvement.

[1]"Shop Management" ASME 24 (1903), 1417-1418.

[2]Nevins, Alan "Ford," The Times, The Man, The Company," New York: Scribners, 1954, Page 468.

[3]Arnold, H. L. and Faurote, F. L. "Ford Methods and Ford Shops," New York: Arno, 1972.

[4]Arnold, Op. Cit., Pp. 106-110.

[5]Sloan, A. P. "My Years with General Motors," New York: Doubleday, 1964.

[6]Arnold, Op. Cit., iii.

[7]Arnold, Op. Cit., P. 41.

[8]Arnold, Op. Cit., P. 271.

[9]Halberstan, D. "The Reckoning," New York: Morrow, 1986.

CHAPTER 2

THE MARKETING ERA IN AMERICA

The last chapter closed on Ford's absolute refusal, as late as 1924, to significantly improve a design which had been frozen since 1908. The improving taste and wealth of consumers, and the opportunity for improvement based on new technology, ushered in a new age. To understand the power of marketing and technology, let us again take up our story.

Alfred P. Sloan: President of General Motors

By 1920 Ford had 45% of the market and earned $53 million after tax. During the recession of 1921, Ford increased his grip to 60% and increased his profit to $75 million. By contrast, General Motors sales dropped from $567 million in 1920 to $304 million in 1921, with an operating loss of $38 million. Chevrolet sales in 1920 were 134,117 units, and in 1921 they dropped to 58,080. In 1920 Ford sales were 690,755, and in 1921 they soared to 933,720.

Alfred Sloan commented at the time:[1]

"With Ford in almost complete possession of the low price field, it would have been suicidal to compete with him head on. No conceivable amount of capital short of the U.S. Treasury could have sustained the losses required to take volume away at his game."

Alfred Sloan reasoned as follows: Ford's Model T car supplied utility transportation, reliable but not fancy. Until early in the 1920's there were few used cars. Most customers were buying their first car, and they generally bought new Model T's. When buyers bought their second car, they would trade in the Model T and would want to buy something better. Thus, Sloan reasoned, these second time buyers would be a good market for a car slightly better than a Model T and priced slightly higher. He added features to the new Chevrolet "K" model such as a self starter and closed bodies. DuPont developed the

Duco paint, allowing a wide choice of durable colors. Sloan was using the possibilities of new technology to enhance the appeal of his product. He offered a variety of features on Chevrolet. Sloan further reasoned that buyers who wanted utility transportation would buy a used car, not a new Model T. By 1925 the strategy was working, as the following table illustrates:

UNIT SALES VOLUME[10]

| | Chevrolet | | Ford | |
| | Unit | Unit | Unit | Unit |
Year	Volume	Price	Volume	Price
1925	481,000	735	1,652,000	580
1926	692,000	695	1,379,000	565
1927	940,277	645	364,000	495

In 1928, 1930, and 1935 Ford regained leadership, but in all other years trailed Chevrolet unit sales. In 1921, a nearly bankrupt General Motors which had negligible unit volume in the low price market faced Ford's immense cash reserves and 60% market share. Sloan's marketing strategy was the primary vehicle for success.

GM used Flow Manufacturing in Final Assembly. But subassemblies were built using batches for inventory. General Motors never approached Ford's Model T production results in either cost or inventory turns. However, product diversity acted to stimulate customer demand.

How do you maintain that stimulation? Sloan again provided another innovation: the annual model change. Prior to Sloan's policy, changes were brought in piecemeal. In fact, his marketing vice-president, Richard Grant, opposed the concept of the annual model change, saying

"Shall we have yearly model changes. I say no . . . we ought to make all changes invisible without announcement."

Grant was reflecting prevailing thought. Now that we have had over 60 years of annual model changes, it's difficult to believe it was a matter for debate. Yet who has not felt a sense of interest in seeing the new fall line-up of cars? Who can say it doesn't stimulate demand? Sloan's conquest of Ford against seemingly impossible odds show that the sovereignty of customer demand must be the primary focus in any business. By making use of the newest technology to enhance products, and by doing an adequate job in manufacturing, Sloan achieved a balance which made GM one of the most successful companies in history.

Thomas J. Watson, Sr.: IBM

Mr. Watson started his career as a salesman. He rose rapidly, and was prominent in the stellar performance of NCR.

In 1914 Watson was hired to manage a pitiful conglomeration which became IBM. The company sold meat slicers, cheese slicers, scales, time recorders and . . . tabulating machines. Watson built a well-trained, well-attired sales force, and focused R&D on tabulating machines. He sold off the cheese and meat slicer and scales business. He instituted an "open door" policy to all workers, and personally rectified hundreds of complaints, generally favoring the worker. The first ten years were up and down for the little company, but in the early twenties, tabulating machine sales began to grow, and profits soared.

Watson's major contribution to our story is in his strategy of using product diversity to stimulate sales in periods of depression as well as good times.

The Great Depression to Watson was "a golden decade full of risks and boldness. . . ."[2]

All of his ideas, and his spirit embodied in the company to which he had given his life, were put on trial. In the end, Watson had made a fortune, his voice was heard throughout the world, and the foundations laid for an industrial giant.

When the depression hit in 1929 IBM was caught in an expansive mood. As business worsened, Watson counseled,

"We can drop with business, or we can build a bridge. Let's build a bridge."

He expanded the sales force and R&D effort. In 1930, the office equipment industry suffered a 50% decline, but IBM held steady. In 1932, Watson paid tribute to his R&D department:

"It was the development work of the men of these departments during the preceding years that made it possible for us to carry on during the last three years of stress. We have been able to carry on and keep our people employed because the men in our engineering department are constantly giving us new and better products. These additions to our line have enabled us to put on more salesmen and broaden our fields of activity . . . That is why today we are breaking ground for a new building entirely devoted to research and engineering work."[3]

Watson's R&D effort paid off when his newly developed tabulating machine won the Social Security contract of 1935. In a speech in 1936, Watson pointed out that 50% of IBM sales were for products not in existence at the time of the Crash.

By 1938, Watson had doubled the number of salesmen over the 1929 figure, and doubled sales in the face of the most titanic economic disaster in modern history.

Increasing product diversity and a powerful sales force stimulated sales and beat the tide. If everyone had had Watson's courage, need there have been a Depression?

In the early years of computers, IBM was not a technology leader. But the focus on solving customer problems and the powerful sales force gave IBM the time to surpass Univac, the founder of the industry. IBM was changing from mechanical business machine technology to electronic technology, a difficult transition. By the 1970's, IBM had become universally recognized as a source of advanced computer, semi-conductor, and materials technology.

During the 1960-1980 time period, IBM essentially developed most of the products which advanced the industry. Profit margins were thus very high. In such an environment, the emphasis is on development and marketing. Manufacturing cost was less important than being able to meet production schedules, and the fast growing customer demand. The increase of effective competition in the late 1970's caused IBM to set the new goal of becoming the low cost producer. In the 1980's, IBM has increasingly focused on low cost, high quality production. Continuous Flow Manufacturing has been highly developed, and applied in several plants. Quoting from the 1985 IBM Annual Report (p. 3):

As a result of our history of continuous investments in more efficient plants and equipment, unit manufacturing costs reached an all-time low.

Thus IBM is in the midst of another challenge: to become the low cost producer. In later chapters we shall provide some insights into this effort.

Summary

The success of companies who were guided by marketing led to the wide acceptance of the need for a diverse product line. Manufacturing strategy had been fundamental to Ford's success. In the American Marketing era, R&D and Marketing dominated strategic thinking. Manufacturing became an execution arm of the company, not a partner in developing corporate strategy. Manufacturing's job was to be able to meet the rapidly growing demand, with cost a secondary factor. The rigid Ford production method appeared to be incompatible with a diverse product line, and was largely discarded in favor of the Batch production method. To fully appreciate the cost advantages of Continuous Flow we must first understand the hidden weaknesses of Batch Production, which is the subject of the next chapter.

---

[1]Sloan, Op. Cit., P. 162
[2]T. G. Belden, *The Lengthening Shadow,* (Boston: Little, Brown, 1962), P. 160.
[3]Watson, T. J., "Men, Minutes, and Money." New York: IBM Corp., 1934, Pg. 662.

CHAPTER 3

THE WASTEFUL FACTORY

At mid century, marketing had come into its rightful place in the highest councils of most business enterprises. The need for a company to be responsive to customer needs was sharpened by improved communication, advertising, and increasing national wealth. Virtually all companies correctly accepted the need for a broad and diverse product line. Ford's inflexible methods were history.

Batch Production "solved" the problems of manufacturing a product with many variations. In Batch Production, a large lot of each type of sub-assembly is built for both present and future needs, most of which are stored in inventory. When products are being assembled for customers, sub-assemblies are withdrawn from the inventory. Thus, production of products for customers are not affected by long setup time. The high cost of a long setup time is offset by building a large lot, thus spreading its cost over many units.

A few industries, like automotive, used continuous flow for Final Assembly. But most products and sub-assemblies were manufactured in large batches for inventory, not for immediate use. This fact was common to assembly as well as process plants. Because Batch production is able to build a diverse product with low labor cost it was unconsciously accepted as the *only* viable method. IBM, in fact, refers to Batch production as "Business as Usual!"

Taylor's concept that management was responsible for developing efficient work methods and machines was not discarded, and continued to guide Manufacturing Engineers. But the emphasis had changed: Manufacturing Engineering tended to focus on the work at individual Operations, rather than on the flow of the product as required by the Ford System. The reason is simple, product doesn't flow in Batch Production. Although some attention was paid to plant layout, it had ceased to become the guiding determinant of all processes and operations which was the case with Ford.

Thus Batch production became the dominant American manufacturing approach. Batch production has, however, hidden costs which result in much higher total cost. These hidden costs were not recognized. The Ford system was considered just as applicable to manufacturing as Zeppelins are to air transportation: curious technology from a bygone era.

We will analyze a company making the transition from job shop to Batch Production. This example will show why Batch Production was so successful and hence popular. Its hidden dangers will then be discussed. This example will also illustrate the immense profit leverage of focused manufacturing engineering efforts.

One of the authors was the President of International Power Machines. This electronics company builds Uninterruptible Power Supplies (UPS), used to protect critical equipment from power failures. The industry began its growth in the 1970's, and interestingly enough, the principal customers were electrical utility companies. These companies used UPS to protect vital instrumentation in nuclear and fossil power plants. The use of UPS to protect on-line computers was a small but growing business.

Like most of our competitors we sold what we could to customer specifications. In the case of electrical utility companies, they and their engineering firms wrote highly detailed specifications requiring special features and materials.

Virtually no two UPS were alike, and hence were built one at a time on a job shop basis. The company made money in 1976, and was losing money in 1977 due to a large nuclear plant job. The company had a big backlog, but was always late on delivery. Mechanical parts didn't fit, and we had serious problems with quality in the factory and in the field. The company's principal power range was generating a low gross profit margin. What would you do?

We went to the public library! We started reading about manufacturing and production, and found a book which identified the three manufacturing methods:

1. *Job Shop: We knew what that was, build each job uniquely.*
2. *"Ford" Production: Long production runs, no product diversity. Impossible in our market.*
3. *Batch Production: Group all like assemblies together in a batch, build for both present and anticipated needs. Spread the large setup cost over many units.*

Batch Production was the obvious choice.

Eliminating Unnecessary Diversity

Because our customers wanted custom features, our engineers had grown up with custom product. Each unit had its own unique wire list, bill of material and module part number. Because all drawings had been custom, engineering was always late in getting paperwork to manufacturing. this led to shortcuts. For example, engineering would use a previous unit as a baseline, then add the changes as "notes." This caused great confusion in manufacturing, and was the source of many defects. In fact, more than 90% of the wiring was always the same, because it functionally controlled the equipment. Yet *all* wiring was custom. Despite some opposition, we finally decided to make all functional wiring identical for each power range. This was called the Primary Wiring. Customer specials would be accomplished by a Secondary Wiring list which ran in parallel to the Primary, but had its own connectors. Variations in wire length were accomplished by dash numbers. We did not lose the ability to meet custom requirements. This same logic was extended to instrumentation, circuit breakers, power wires, etc.

We suddenly realized we had built everything one-at-a-time even though they could be standardized at least up to the unique custom features. In discussions with our engineers, we found that we could mechanically standardize our principle product, replacing seven separate mechanical designs with one.

We had read Frederick Taylor's book, and were able to hire an experienced Manufacturing Engineer with Taylor's stamp. In addition to standardizing the design, we wanted to improve the operations by which it is built.

The effort at operations improvement went forward with gusto. For example, in watching the work on the shop floor, the Manufacturing Engineer found that the operation of building an alarm relay panel took 12 hours. The terminal blocks were so close together that the assemblers had to "sew" the wires past the blocks. By enlarging the case 1 inch and making the wire harness on an external fixture the total time was cut to 30 minutes!

A prototype of the new "baseline" unit was built, with three engineers watching and locating every problem. For the first time, they worked with design engineers on the shop floor.

Detailed work instructions were developed with photographs and clear, simple text detailing how each sub-assembly was put together. All wire lengths were measured, tabularized with terminations, and prepared at a special work station. Instrumentation panels became a separate assembly. In short, the product was standardized, the work was sub-divided down, and specialized work stations developed with jigs and tooling to efficiently build in batches.

We left a blank panel on the machine to incorporate any special features that customers would want at extra cost, above and beyond the standard product. We decided to build the standard unit complete and tested, and incorporate any special features on the blank panel later. In the past, custom features had been incorporated into the design of the machine, and had affected the assembly number of each sub-assembly they touched. This caused the creation of a special set of batches, high labor and paperwork costs. Now, only the blank panel part number was affected. Its Drawing and Bill of Material showed all changes. The cost of both the "baseline" standard product and custom features was thus reduced.

We knew that some of our customers, like nuclear power plants, could not accept our standard product, even with variations. They amounted to 35% of our sales, so it was with great concern that we decided to refuse further nuclear business. We were to be tempted, however. No sooner had we made this policy public than we were offered a large repeat order for a nuclear plant. We had just read Wickham Skinner's book, *Manufacturing in the Corporate Strategy*, on the need for a focused factory. Despite all the pleas from marketing, we felt that it would entirely defocus our efforts.

A commitment is not a commitment unless you are willing to suffer to keep it.

As labor cost was reduced, we did not need as many workers. We took the most motivated workers out of production and put them in Manufacturing Engineering department as Assistant ME. This gave us more implementation strength to build new prototypes, wire harness boards, etc. Like all creative work, Manufacturing Engineering is "5% inspiration and 95% perspiration." These Assistant ME provided more leverage on the efforts of our professional Manufacturing Engineering staff.

Sales in general were falling, and with the company losing money, a cutback in expense was necessary. We believed that our new approach would be successful, and that we would need these trained people. The approach taken was to reduce all salaried wages by 10%, which allowed us to keep our best hourly workers.

But to whom could we sell this standard product? In 1977, IBM announced the 3033, a powerful machine aimed at on-line processing at a good price. Everybody had made noises, but we believed that IBM was going to make on-line processsing a wide spread reality rather than something just for airlines. We moved toward computer users and away from electric utilities.

As the company withdrew from Job Shop custom design to a standard product, the need for Product Engineering personnel decreased. They were well educated personnel who knew our product well, made big salaries, and who were no longer needed. We moved some of these Engineers to R&D to help develop more products. Three more engineers were moved to Marketing, and later were among the company's Ten Best Field Salesmen. Developing a diverse product line and a powerful sales force is better for the employee, the customer and the company.

Sales quickly expanded as we focused on the computer market. We started out with batches of 5 units, then expanded to lots of 10, 20 and finally to batch sizes for mechanical parts of 100 units. Within 8 months Direct labor cost fell from $4200 per unit to under $1800, and quality improved. The Gross Profit Margin of the company's principal product increased from 16% to over 40%. The company grew fivefold from 1977 to 1980, moving from a 5% loss to a pre-tax profit of 18% on sales. Salaries were restored, the 10% accumulated cut was repaid, as well as significant bonuses. The improved manufacturing and engineering methods allowed us to ship 50% more product per person per year. The company went public in 1980, and was subsequently sold to a large company.

With such good performance, why would anyone complain about Batch production? When sales leveled off in 1981, inventory continued to grow. In 1982, the company introduced new products, and inventory grew further, although sales were down. Fortunately the company had the cash reserves to weather the storm.

Powerful as the Batch Production process was in reducing direct labor cost, it has one terrible flaw: danger of excess inventory and resulting hidden Manufacturing Overhead and Quality cost. To reduce costs you build in large batches. Basically, we assumed that the time to setup a machine or prepare for a batch for assemblies was fixed. If you setup and build one piece, and then do something else, your one unit cost includes a sometimes lengthy setup cost. So to avoid high cost, you build in large batches, thus the setup time is spread over many units.

But what lot size should you select? Obviously you want the lot size that yields the lowest labor cost. The lowest cost lot size can be calculated using Wilson's Economic Lot Size (ELS) formula which is taught in all college courses on Manufacturing.

The Economic Lot Size formula balances two costs, inventory cost and setup cost. According to Wilson, the inventory cost is the interest cost of keeping the value of units in inventory. Thus the inventory cost rises directly with the number of units and the time they are held in inventory. The setup cost to prepare a machine or assembly operation is generally not dependent on the number of units to be built. Thus the setup cost per unit drops drastically as the lot size is increased. Lets look at an example.

Assume an operation has a setup time of 3 hours, with a burdened cost of $100. Assume we are producing parts with a unit cost (material, labor and overhead) of $10. The interest rate is 10% per annum. We expect to use 1000 parts per year, 20 parts per week.

The Economic Lot Size Formula is:

$$\text{Lowest Cost Lot Size} = \sqrt{\frac{2\ (\text{Setup Cost})\ (\text{Usage})}{(\text{Interest Rate})\ (\text{Unit Cost})}}$$

$$\text{Lowest Cost Lot Size} = \sqrt{\frac{2\ (100)(1000)}{(0.10)(10)}} = 447\ \text{Units}$$

Thus, the ELS formula yields a lot size equal to a 6 month production requirement at 20 units per week. The unit cost is $10 plus the setup cost of $100 spread over 447 units, for a total of $10.22. If we only built the 20 units required for this weeks production, our total cost would be the unit cost of $10 plus the setup cost of $100 spread over 20 units. This yields a total cost of $15 per unit, a 47% premium. Thus the ELS quantity would appear to save us a great deal of cost.

However, assuming you built the batch size of 447, it must all be inspected, putting a severe step load on the inspector. If the lot is bad it must be scrapped, for a loss of $4570. Usually, the lot cannot be immediately inspected. When defects are discovered, it is often too late to find out the cause, making prevention of a reoccurrence nearly impossible. If some of the tested parts are found to be defective, they must be reworked and retested. Defects that cannot be reworked must be scrapped. This increases cost and effectively reduces production capacity.

In the rush to build the lot, defects are common. Because the lot is so large, inspection is often done by sampling, which inevitably allows some defects to slip through. *Sampling inspection*, it was rationalized, is as good as 100% inspection because it avoids inspector fatigue and resulting errors. However, as defects move on in production, the cost of *rework* escalates until *warranty cost* and *lost customer goodwill* are experienced. The cost of *test, rework, inspection, scrap, lost production capacity* and *warranty cost* is the Hidden Quality Cost which is silently absorbed into Manufacturing Overhead cost.

Assuming that the lot is good, you must deal with 447 parts. Now 447 parts take up 22 times more space than do the 20 parts needed this week. Thus, you will send 427 to the *stockroom*. They must first be *transported* down a space consuming *forklift* alley to the stockroom. Expensive *material handling equipment* may be purchased. There they are *counted, entered* into *inventory*, and *shelved* in their space. Hopefully the stockroom is laid out around the ELS quantities so there is a space for the full lot. Otherwise, the parts may be jumbled and lost, causing expensive *Retrieval* Labor. Assuming the stockroom has been properly laid out, you will have 22 times the needed *space* tied up for no productive purpose. The next week, when more parts are needed, they must be *requisitioned, retrieved, counted, issued,* and *transported*. This cycle will be repeated 22 times, and its hidden cost silently absorbed. The cost of 22 times needed space will be *paid for, heated, cooled* and *lighted*. The conclusion we reach is that the Overhead Cost *increases linearly with increasing Batch size!* There is an economy of scale in direct labor in producing a large batch (spreading setup cost). There is no economy of scale in overhead.

Perhaps expensive Capital Equipment such as an automated storage and retrieval system will be purchased. We will refer to these costs as the Hidden Inventory Cost, as opposed to visible inventory cost due to interest.

Finally, having built this lowest cost batch size, which amounts to a six months requirement, you must be concerned that the parts may be *lost, broken* or become *obsolete.* In the name of Direct Labor efficiency, supply is no longer related to real demand, large hidden costs are absorbed, and great risks of loss accepted. Not all Batch operations followed Wilson's formula faithfully, but all of them built present, future, and speculative amounts to form their lot size.

Batch Production has the further problem that it does not provide a rational basis for selecting the production capacity of capital equipment or needed manpower. Each lot produced is larger than current need, and hence most of it goes to the stockroom. Each assembly line withdraws a large lot of material from stock, processes it, and returns most of the product to stock for removal by subsequent processes. There is no continuous "timing" between Operations, but there are frequent production crises. To keep product moving to customers, each Operation must be able to respond to huge peak demands to build a large lot, a few pieces of which are immediately needed by Final Assembly. But to obtain the lowest labor cost, the whole lot must be built, or the cost of another setup would be incurred. Thus, when operating under Batch Production, a company tends to buy "Supermachines" which have the production capacity to quickly build large lots. In our example, we must build 447 units when only 20 are required to meet customer demand. This results in a machine capacity twenty times greater than the rate of consumption of that product by Final Assembly. "Supermachines" are more expensive than a smaller machine which could just keep up with Final Assembly needs. Thus, there is a *waste of Capital Investment* due to excessive machine capacity. The manpower assigned to each Operation also is influenced by the peak capacity demands of large lots, and tends toward *excess manpower capacity.* Despite these excess expenses, "Lot Splitting" is still common. To keep production going, small "rush" orders are run in at high cost. This firefighting effort requires even more manpower capability.

Excess capacity is visible in many companies as the end of the month "push," in which more than half of monthly shipments are made in the last week. This intense effort is often followed by a period of slack activity in the new month. This can only be the result of plant capacity in excess of the average need due to customer orders. This excess Hidden Capacity is, of course, a hidden waste factor.

Neglecting setup time, the time to build a batch of 447 parts is approximately 20 times as great as to build a batch of 20 parts. The time to build a batch is called the Cycle Time. Thus the Cycle Time rises linearly with Batch size. The Cycle Time of a product is, of course, important in being able to supply the specific product desired by the customer. Thus, the longer the Cycle Time, the less responsive to changing customer demands. Large batches lead to slow Manufacturing Cycle Time and poor customer response.

Finally, companies are being faced with an increasing rate of technological change and decreased product life span. Thus new products, or Engineering Change Orders (ECO) may render a large inventory of the batch obsolete. The result is that a company is faced with significant rework and scrap costs.

None of the italicized efforts items add value to the product. None of these costs are included in the Economic Lot Size Formula. We shall later see that most of this effort can be eliminated as unnecessary waste. ***Obviously the source of most of our trouble is that we build in large lots.*** If we could somehow economically build in small lots, much waste would be avoided. In our example, if we could economically build 20 units as cheaply as 447, all of the waste costs defined above would be eliminated. We would build the 20 parts, and deliver them directly to the Operation where they are being used. In Ford's case, the next Operation was an arms length away. Thus, economic small lot production could achieve lower cost production.

The Hidden Factory

What would you think of a factory into which material and manpower flowed, but which never supplied any output product? We would all consider it a total waste. Yet the Hidden Inventory Cost, the Hidden Quality Cost, the Hidden Capacity Cost constitute a Hidden Factory.

Each Batch Production Factory has a Hidden Factory, fully manned and functioning (often on overtime), which consumes labor,

36

material, and capital, and opposes the Productive Factory at every turn.

How do we treat the Hidden Factory from an accounting point of view? Most of its costs are scattered among a half dozen accounts including Manufacturing Overhead, Inventory Shrinkage, Obsolescence, Interest Cost, and Warranty Cost. Manufacturing Overhead includes the cost of plant space, utilities, depreciation of capital equipment, rework, known scrap, overtime. It includes the people, cost of Stockroom, Purchasing, Production Control, Supervision, Quality Control. Manufacturing Overhead is three to six times greater in Batch Production than with Continuous Flow. For a $100 million company, a Continuous Flow plant would have one half the space and typically save $12 million on Manufacturing Overhead.

Inventory Shrinkage and Obsolescence is due to lost parts, broken parts, unknown scrap, and unusable remnants of large batches. The interest cost is the cost of financing the excess inventory and capital equipment. Typical Batch operations turn their inventory in the range of four times per year. Continuous Flow Manufacturing (CFM) operations turn their inventory 15-70 times per year, depending on how diligently they apply the CFM tools. For a $100 million company, just the inventory reduction alone would save $1 million per year. Known Warranty cost in many companies run 3-5% of sales. Under CFM, the cost will run less than a half percent, plus the additional profit margins available from satisfied customers.

In the next few chapters, we will show you how CFM achieves these remarkable results. You will then see why a CFM plant will have a 20-30% cost advantage over Batch production.

Summary

In this chapter, we traced the reasons for the popularity of Batch production. Batch production is clearly superior to Job Shop production in quality, uniformity and efficiency. Batch production appeared to be superior to Ford's methods in that it allowed product variety.

The hidden cost of Batch production arises primarily because Manufacturing Overhead rises linearly with Batch size. There is no economy of scale in Overhead. This results in a large number of

Production Control, Quality Control, Stockroom, Purchasing and Material Handling personnel. It also results in large depreciation charges due to excessive Machine Capacity and Plant Size. Finally, the lumpiness of demand requires high peak capacity, which causes continuous excess personnel needs to meet these end-of-month demands.

CHAPTER 4

THE NEW MANUFACTURING REVOLUTION

The time was 1949, the place Japan. The country was still dispirited by the first defeat in its history, and by the continuing military occupation. Drug addiction, which was nil before the War, had spread to over a million Japanese. The industrial base of the country was still shattered, and had an international reputation for making junk. Powerful Left Wing labor leaders were fomenting strikes, crippling productivity and threatening to destroy the remnant of private enterprise.

The Toyota Motor company, like the rest of Japan, tottered at the brink of bankruptcy. Should such a country even be in an industry as sophisticated as car production? In 1950, Toyota's labor time to produce a car was nearly 10 times that of Detroit. Annual Japanese car production was 30,000 units, about a half day's worth of Detroit's output!

The Toyota President, Kirchiro Toyoda, set the goal of catching the Americans. While Mr. Toyoda wanted to achieve Henry Ford's low cost, he did not want to restrict Toyota to a single model of car. Rather, he set the goal of developing a manufacturing system which would attain low cost but would also allow product diversity. He believed that a wide product line was needed to stimulate demand. The manufacturing system pioneered by Toyota was an adaptation of Henry Ford's methods, and a rejection of Batch Production.

What have been the results? In 1952 it took Toyota ten man months to produce a vehicle. By 1985 it took 0.2 man months, a 50 times improvement. Counting all variations of body types, engines, paint, options, etc., there are nearly 10 million types of Toyota which a customer might order. Yet Toyota can accept an entirely custom order and deliver the car in less than one week to a Japanese customer. Toyota turns its inventory 70 times per year, compared to 8-15 times for U.S. car manufacturers. The amount of labor time to produce a car is less than one third of the U.S. figure. How is this achievement attained? Was it Robots? More dedicated workers?

For the most part, Japanese factories are not filled with highly sophisticated equipment and do not make extensive use of intelligent robots and automation equipment. The general level of technical sophistication in Japanese manufacturing is not dramatically different from that of the United States. The Japanese do not run this equipment for long hours or at higher production rates than U.S. factories. Physical plant and work force considerations have not been major factors in their success.

However, in comparing the number of Manufacturing Overhead personnel per car produced, the American plant has nearly six times that of the Japanese plant. The amount of space consumed per production unit is three times as great. Fully two thirds of the productivity advantage is in lower Manufacturing Overhead cost. In other words, the Direct Labor Force, the Productive Factory is not our biggest problem. It's the Hidden Factory which supplies no output, that is the primary American disadvantage.

Under Batch Production methods, the Hidden Factory cannot be assaulted by Robots, nor reduced by a more productive work force. The reason for this is that the Hidden Factory isn't producing anything, it is just consuming.

Thus, the heart of the "Just-In-Time" system is the elimination of waste in its broadest sense: Anything that doesn't add value to the product is waste. This includes all the operations of the Hidden Factory: storing, counting, transporting, rejecting, scrap, rework, inspecting, excess capacity, etc. A production method which achieves these waste elimination goals has been studied in Chapter I, the Ford system.

The Japanese were fortunate in receiving and accepting the guidance of two distinguished American consultants, W. E. Deming and J. M. Juran. Their philosophy that lowest cost can only be achieved through high quality was accepted by the Japanese, and is part of the "warp and woof" of Continuous Flow manufacturing. These lectures were attended not only by Japanese engineers, but by the CEO and all top officers. Their CEO's had the humility to learn about manufacturing and quality methods. One of the goals of this book is to present even more superior material for American CEO's.

Original Toyota Implementation

The first modern attempt to implement Just In Time in the production of a broad product line was carried out by the Toyota Motor Company beginning in 1950. At this early date computers were a thing of the future, and entirely manual methods were employed to locate waste. We will first describe the Toyota implementation as a point of reference, as this is the method which has been widely attempted in the U.S. We will then describe the problems of the Toyota method and their solution, pioneered in the U.S. by IBM.

We have learned that much of the hidden costs are related to the Overhead needed to build, manage and store the slow turning inventory. The other primary component of hidden cost is due to the waste of defects, scrap, rework and warranty cost. In the next chapter, we will learn that defect prevention is nearly impossible with large lots of material. Defects, in turn, generate hidden cost in the form of scrap, rework, extra tests, warranty cost, and loss of customer satisfaction. On both counts, we know that small lot sizes must be a key factor in obtaining the lowest cost. We also know that, if we lower lot sizes but keep the long setup times fixed, output per day will fall and cost will increase. We may spend more time setting up than operating on the material. The Operation time per unit might then be too low to keep up with the schedule. Similar arguments could be made for time spent in Rework, and Transport time between operations, etc.

Clearly, we must develop a system to find and correct problems which are caused by small lot production. The method of finding these problems which was developed by Toyota was entirely manual and experimental, and begins by relaying out the plant.

Process Flow Improvement

Toyota copies Henry Ford in first relaying out the entire plant for continuous flow. Thus each sub-assembly line contains all the machines and processes needed to complete the sub-assembly. The machines and processes are thus re-arranged physically in the sequence of fabrication. This often requires considerable expense in moving or duplicating equipment. This is necessary in the Toyota method, as it eliminates transportation time between operations and allows one to isolate the remaining setup, operation and rework time at the various operations. Obviously relaying out the plant is a major disruption which we would like to avoid if possible.

The Pull or "Kanban" System

One first levels the customer delivery schedule so that about the same amount of work is done each day. By leveling the production rate, each operation will have about the same amount of work each day. In fact, this is merely an attempt to schedule at a rate which is consistent with the inevitable outcome. Leveling recognizes that you cannot vary the daily output of an Operation significantly.

The Pull System makes possible the goal of avoiding the production of large lots of material and incurring the wastes described in the previous chapter. Using the Pull System, only the final assembly or process receives the customer orders. Final assembly then demands the required sub-assemblies or materials from upstream operations and processes. Each process sends the demanded product to final assembly, and then rebuilds only the quantity taken. The discipline of the Pull System prevents the wastes of over-production. Because of long setup time at a particular operation, the percentage of time spent on setup will rise, and the time spent on operations in actually building the product will fall. This may reduce output below that needed to satisfy customer demand. Such an occurrence is used by Toyota to trigger Manufacturing Engineering efforts to reduce the setup time at the offending operation, or to reduce the operation time, etc. Toyota pioneered the Four Step Rapid Setup method. This method allows the reduction of setup cost by 90%, making small lot production economical. This Four Step Method is discussed in the next chapter.

In the Toyota method, you start reducing lot sizes until problems surface at a given operation, then you attack those problems. The danger is that too rapid a lot size reduction may result in simultaneous problems. This can restrict output while problems are being resolved. Nevertheless, this was the only approach possible using all manual methods.

Production control of shop work orders was achieved using the

"Kanban" card. Kanban is Japanese for visible record. The customer schedule is given only to Final Assembly which converts the Bill of Materials into a demand for sub-assemblies. This sub-assembly demand is written on a card for each part number. The card is given to the appropriate sub-assembly department which then builds only the quantity needed to replace those taken. The Kanban demand is placed on each previous sub-assembly station, and ripples back to raw stock. The same approach is used in process industries such as chemical and semiconductor plants. In the Toyota system, sub-assembly work orders are not generated by the computer (MRP II), but only by Kanban cards. In practice the Kanban is represented by a container or rack which holds the Kanban quantity. We shall later show what factors influence this quantity. In the Toyota system, an Operation has a Kanban container corresponding to each product built at the Operation. This can lead to difficulties with a product having thousands of variations. This difficulty is resolved by means of the Computer Kanban method described below.

Defect Prevention

One of the major principles of the Toyota system is that defects must not be allowed to pass through the system. No one will quarrel with that. The teeth of the statement is that, if any worker notes a defect, he or she is empowered to shut down the line. The line will remain shut down until the source of the defect is removed.

Thus the production output may be restricted at the outset of the program. Defect Prevention methods have been developed which make the re-occurrence of defects impossible or highly unlikely. These methods are one of the most interesting parts of CFM, and are described in Chapter 7.

Vendor Material

Material is scheduled from vendors in syncronism with demands but only shipped upon actual need. Shipments in small lots every day is the most obvious but least important cost reduction element of the Toyota system. Unfortunately, it has attracted the most attention and caused "Just-In-Time" to be regarded as an inventory reduction program, rather than a Continuous Flow system aimed at low cost, defect free production.

Summary of the Improvement Tools

The Pull System: The Pull System is a discipline which allows the production line to build only that which is needed to fill a firm customer order. In this way the wastes of Batch production are eliminated.

Rapid Setup: The Pull System demands the ability to build in small lots economically. As we say in Chapter 3, this effectively means that we must be able to significantly reduce the setup time. A 90% reduction in setup cost can typically be achieved using the four step method described in the next chapter.

Defect Prevention: A major source of waste is due to scrap, rework, warranty cost and customer dissatisfaction. These waste costs cannot be eliminated by inspection and test. Rather, a system of prevention is employed, as described in Chapter 7.

Operation Improvement: This tool eliminates the waste motion associated with the actual building of the product. It uses methods that are very similar to the rapid setup method, and is described in the next chapter.

Process Flow Improvement: If the transportation and queue time between operations is long, additional inventory will be trapped in the pipeline. This will require larger than necessary lots to keep the production process running. To eliminate this problem, the operations are moved close together, and placed in the fabrication sequence.

Implementation of the Toyota System in America

One of the most famous successes is the Greeley, Colorado experience of Hewlett-Packard, in which cost was reduced, cycle time improved, inventory turns tripled, etc. The people involved were both dedicated and brilliant. HP is one of the best managed corporations in America. But if one looks at Hewlett-Packard corporate wide, 1985 inventory turns were less than four. Just-In-Time has only been implemented by a handful of divisions.

Thus we see many U.S. companies who have a few lines running "Just-In-Time," but the corporation as a whole still shows low inventory turns and hence high waste. Why? Because the Toyota system requires a long implementation period or exceptional management. The reason for the difficulties with the Toyota system is that one first must move operations into a flow line. You then find the problems by lot size reductions which may restrict output. This lack of a consistent method has led to articles entitled, "Too Much JIT Can Spoil the Plant." (Manufacturing Systems, October, 1986). The thrust of the article is that one should keep extra inventory aside to see if the line can really run with the reduced lot sizes. It is the natural defense of a person "bitten" by the Toyota system. What is needed is a system which allows the prediction of problems, determination of the correct lot size, and which doesn't require moving the Workcenters to get started. With such a tool in hand, the implementation of Continuous Flow can be carried out by a methodical and planned effort, free of plant disruption and loss of output.

A further characteristic of American implementation is their lack of thoroughness. Fewer than 10% of JIT implementations use all of the improvement tools. Specifically, Mistake Proof Operations, Designed Experiments, and Rapid Setup have gotten short shrift. These tools will be described in succeeding chapters. This lack of thoroughness in part is due to omissions in the popular books on the subject. It is also due in part to the lack of knowledge as to which tool to apply where, i.e., thoroughness is inhibited by the trial and error nature of the Toyota system. Most applications install the Pull System and Process Flow Improvement and call that JIT. The total cost reduction potential is thus seldom realized.

Summary of the Implementation Problems of Just In Time

The JIT System has three major problems

1. *Plant Re-Layout:* The first step is to move all the workcenters into a flow line. Thus one applies the process flow improvement tool immediately even though transport time may not be the most important problem. Moving workcenters is an expensive and disruptive process, which

should only be carried out if and when it is necessary. As we shall see moving the operations and workcenters is generally the last effort required.

2. ***Production Restriction:*** The second step in the JIT System is trial and error lot size reductions to discover which workcenters need the application of an improvement tool. The danger is that too large a lot size reduction may restrict production output.

3. ***Range of Application:*** JIT derives its information by trial and error lot size reductions. If a manufacturer builds a broad product line in small lots, JIT is unable to direct the improvement activities. JIT is thus restricted in range of application to high volume manufacture.

Continuous Flow Manufacturing: A Step Ahead of JIT

The availability of Line Analysis Programs makes possible a more rapid reduction of cost, and improvement of quality, than was possible with the trial and error methods of JIT. Line Analysis allows one to predict which workcenters require the application of an improvement tool, and in which priority.

A good way of understanding the power of Line Analysis is to compare the manufacturing Process to a boat crossing a lake. The successful manufacture of the product is shown in Fig. 4.1 to be like the boat safely crossing the lake. The water covers submerged rocks. The height of the water is the level of inventory or Lot size. If the Lot Size is big enough, production output will meet customer demand. Using Line Analysis, we see that the first rock surfaces at operation 10 at a Lot size of 50. Thus we can immediately reduce the Lot size by 50% while Manufacturing Engineering reduces the setup time at operation 10. (Fig. 4.2) To reduce the Lot size below 40, we will have time at operation 4. Notice that transport time is not a problem until a Lot size of 15 is desired. At this point, we would have to re-layout the plant. If such a re-layout is too expensive, and a Lot size of 15 at operation 3 is preferable, you may not wish to disrupt the plant. Typically, Plant Relayout is the last step required, and is often the most difficult. Thus you may elect to put buffer inventory at a few selected operations. This concept was fully developed by IBM

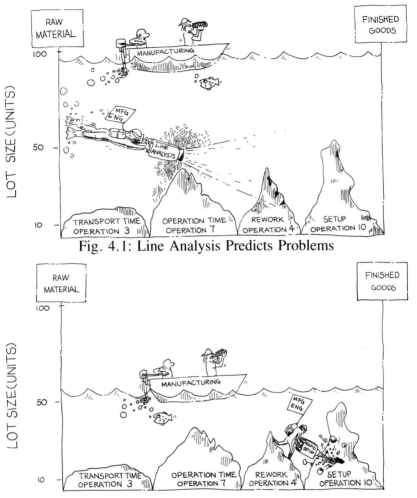

Fig. 4.1: Line Analysis Predicts Problems

Fig. 4.2: Line Analysis Allows Systematic Improvement

and is dealt with in Chapter 10. Buffer inventory may also be used to compensate for machine failure, late delivery, or machines which have a fixed batch size. In practice, the controlled buffer inventories do not severely impact inventory turns. The buffer inventory is known, controlled, and eventually may be eliminated.

As we discussed earlier, the Toyota system uses trial and error to discover the problems. As Lot size and inventory is reduced, the rocks surface. In our example, reducing Lot size by 60% would only expose one rock at operation 10. Reducing the Lot size by 10% more would have simultaneously exposed three rocks (Fig. 4.3), stopping production. In fact, sometimes the hidden rocks are more numerous and higher in the water. Blind Lot size reduction will lead to serious reduction of output. Thus the Toyota method requires very slow implementation, and accounts for the reason it took them twenty years. American industry doesn't have twenty years to spend.

Fig. 4.3: Traditional JIT May Lead to Restricted Production.

Line Analysis

The primary difference between Just in Time and Continuous Flow Manufacturing is in the means of finding which Workstation most needs improvement. That Workstation will be the one that has the worst combination of manufacturing deficiencies such as long setup times, high defect rates, long machine downtimes, slow processing times, etc. Continuous Flow Manufacturing uses Line Analysis to *predict* which Workstation requires the biggest batch and longest cycle times to meet schedule. Line Analysis also calculates the Workstation Cycle time, i.e., the time it takes the Workstation to set up and build all varieties of products required from that Workstation in minimum batch sizes required to meet customer demand. Line Analysis calculates this batch size to be consistent with both the customer demand and the existing manufacturing deficiencies. As improvements are made, Line Analysis will recalculate smaller batch sizes which may be input into MRP or a manual system. The batch or lot size is the quantity of a given product which is produced between consecutive setups. The Algorithms which Line Analysis uses are derived in software training classes.

The batch sizes calculated by Line Analysis are always smaller than those calculated by the Economic Lot Size or Economic Order Quantity (EOQ) formula discussed on page 33. This is usually because the true costs of carrying inventory are understated. When the full cost impact of Engineering Change Orders and resulting rework, scrap, obsolescence, lost production capacity, warehousing and personnel cost are added to interest cost, the batch sizes are closer. Even so, the batch sizes calculated by Line Analysis are significantly smaller. Does this mean that a penalty in high cost must be paid? The answer is no. The lowest cost batch size of the EOQ formula occurs at the minimum of a very shallow curve. You can pick a batch size substantially lower than the EOQ formula and the resulting unit cost increase will be insignificant. The EOQ formula should never be used. It invariably leads to batch sizes far greater than needed, resulting in much longer Workstation and overall Manufacturing cycle times. Line Analysis gives us the batch sizes that are needed to meet customer demand. Production beyond customer demand is a waste. Line Analysis allows one to determine what type of improvement (Rapid Setup, Defect Prevention, Preventive Maintenance, etc.) will be most effective, how much improvement is needed, and what is the safe batch size to meet schedule. Line Analysis can be used to improve a factory in which the batch size is already 1, because it will allow prioritization by cycle time rather than batch size. Thus Continuous Flow Manufacturing can be applied to all manufacturing applications, both high and low volume, broad and narrow product lines, and can be implemented without shutting down production. Line Analysis proceeds by first collecting data on the factory as it is presently operating. The needed data includes:

1. The customer demand for each product
2. The setup times at each Workstation
3. The processing times to produce each unit at each Workstation
4. The percentage of scrap and rework at each Workstation
5. The transport and queue time between each Workstation
6. The amount of machine downtime at each Workstation
7. The amount of human downtime for each process

The minimum amount of information needed is the setup times and the processing times, but more data can be added for higher accuracy. This information is input into the Line Analysis program, CompeteAmerica™. Consider the Printed Circuit Board assembly and solder line shown in fig. 4.4 below.

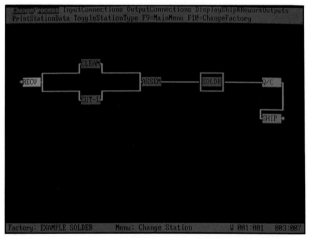

Fig. 4.4: Flow diagram of the Solder process

50

The process consists of 5 Workstations, each building two part numbers. The program can analyze hundreds of Workstations building hundreds of part types, but such a large factory cannot be conveniently shown here. At the left is a Receiving area (RECV), supplying material to the CUT Workstation, which cuts and prepares the component leads, and to the CLEAN Workstation, which prepares the raw printed circuit card. The output of these two Workstations is sent to the ASSEMbly Workstation, which mounts the components on the board. The boards are then sent to the Wave SOLDR machine, which solders the components, and then to Quality Control. The present customer demand is for 120 units of each of the two part types being produced. Production Control releases the batches with a quantity of 500 each. We know that we would like to release the smallest batch size consistent with meeting the schedule of 120 per week of each type. The reason that small batches are preferred is threefold. If an Engineering Change Order is released, a smaller number of boards will need rework. Further, a smaller batch can be completed sooner, giving Final Assembly the variety of boards needed much sooner and speeding up the overall Manufacturing Cycle time. Using a smaller batch size will also free cash tied up in inventory. But what batch size will we pick? The Line Analysis program calculates the minimum batch size that is consistent with a production rate of 120 per week, based on the existing manufacturing deficiencies (long setup, defects, etc).

The data on these Workstations is as follows:

TYPICAL FACTORY DATA
Electronic Printed Circuit Board Assembly

Workstation Type	Setup Time (Hrs)	Direct Labor (Min per part)	Rework %	Transport & Delay (Hrs)	Machine Downtime
Cut Lead	1	8.4	0	0	0
Clean Board	10	5.4	0	0	0
Assembly	1.9	7.2	5	0	0
Solder	1.6	6.6	30	10	5 hrs. out of each 50
Q/C	1.9	7.1	30	0	0

51

This data is entered into a spreadsheet. The menu selection ANALYSIS is selected and the IBM™ AT or better calculates the minimum allowable batch size, shown in fig. 4.5. Note that the SOLDR Workstation requires the biggest batch size of 171 to meet the demand of 120 per week. The batch size of 500 was never needed. One of the problems with SOLDR is that it has a 30% rework rate, tying up $82,080 worth of inventory. Fig. 4.6 shows the results of calculating the Workstation Cycle times.

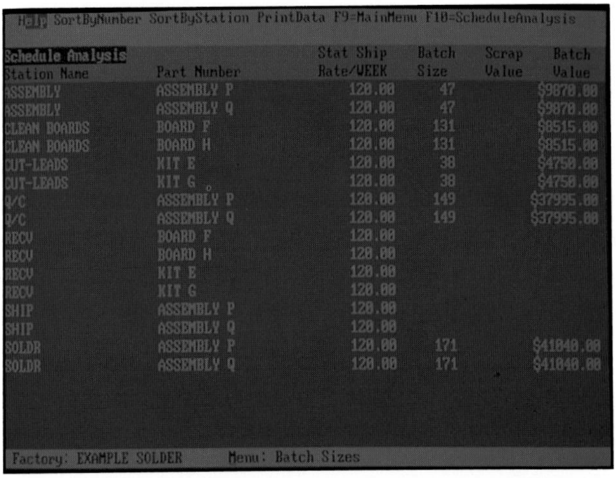

Help SortByNumber SortByStation PrintData F9=MainMenu F10=ScheduleAnalysis

Schedule Analysis Station Name	Part Number	Stat Ship Rate/WEEK	Batch Size	Scrap Value	Batch Value
ASSEMBLY	ASSEMBLY P	120.00	47		$9870.00
ASSEMBLY	ASSEMBLY Q	120.00	47		$9870.00
CLEAN BOARDS	BOARD F	120.00	131		$8515.00
CLEAN BOARDS	BOARD H	120.00	131		$8515.00
CUT-LEADS	KIT E	120.00	38		$4750.00
CUT-LEADS	KIT G	120.00	38		$4750.00
Q/C	ASSEMBLY P	120.00	149		$37995.00
Q/C	ASSEMBLY Q	120.00	149		$37995.00
RECV	BOARD F	120.00			
RECV	BOARD H	120.00			
RECV	KIT E	120.00			
RECV	KIT G	120.00			
SHIP	ASSEMBLY P	120.00			
SHIP	ASSEMBLY Q	120.00			
SOLDR	ASSEMBLY P	120.00	171		$41040.00
SOLDR	ASSEMBLY Q	120.00	171		$41040.00

Factory: EXAMPLE SOLDER Menu: Batch Sizes

Fig. 4.5 Required Batch sizes before improvement

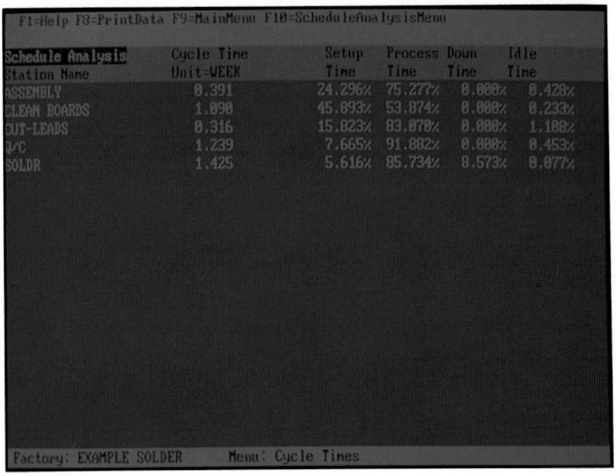

F1=Help F8=PrintData F9=MainMenu F10=ScheduleAnalysisMenu

Schedule Analysis Station Name	Cycle Time Unit=WEEK	Setup Time	Process Time	Down Time	Idle Time
ASSEMBLY	0.391	24.296%	75.277%	0.000%	0.428%
CLEAN BOARDS	1.090	45.893%	53.874%	0.000%	0.233%
CUT-LEADS	0.316	15.823%	83.070%	0.000%	1.108%
Q/C	1.239	7.665%	91.882%	0.000%	0.453%
SOLDR	1.425	5.616%	85.734%	8.573%	0.077%

Factory: EXAMPLE SOLDER Menu: Cycle Times

Fig. 4.6 Workstation Cycle times before improvement

Note that SOLDR has the longest cycle time of 1.4 weeks. It is quite clear that reducing the defect rate at the SOLDR Workstation could greatly improve this Workstation's cycle time. In Chapter 7 we will learn that Designed Experiments are the appropriate method to reduce defects. How much do we need to reduce the defect rate? The goal of Continuous Flow Manufacturing is to improve each Workstation so that they can all process the same batch size in about the same cycle time. Material will then ***flow*** from one Workstation to another, will be immediately checked, processed, tested and used in a final assembly which is shipped to the customer. Each Workstation will then build only what is needed to meet customer demand, not build for inventory. To achieve this goal, we must reduce the defects in SOLDR such that its Workstation Cycle time is comparable to the best in the line, that of CUT LEADS at 0.3 weeks.

How much improvement is needed? Talk to the Operators and Engineers who are responsible for the machine. Based on their knowledge of the defects, they may say that a reasonable goal is to cut the defect rate down to 15%. Entering this value into the spreadsheet and re-running Analysis, one obtains the output shown in fig. 4.7 and 4.8.

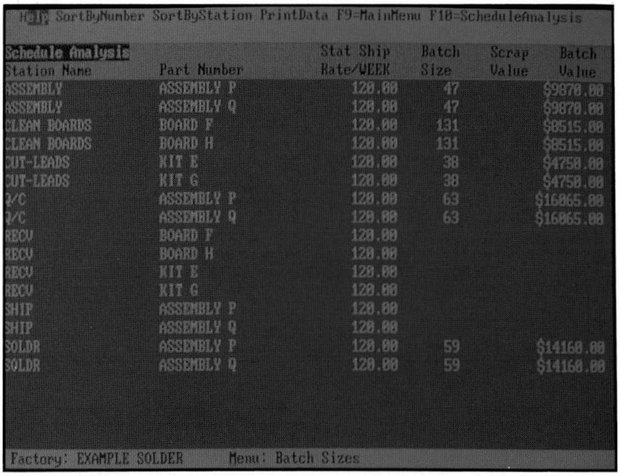
Help SortByNumber SortByStation PrintData F9=MainMenu F10=ScheduleAnalysis

Schedule Analysis

Station Name	Part Number	Stat Ship Rate/WEEK	Batch Size	Scrap Value	Batch Value
ASSEMBLY	ASSEMBLY P	120.00	47		$9870.00
ASSEMBLY	ASSEMBLY Q	120.00	47		$9870.00
CLEAN BOARDS	BOARD F	120.00	131		$8515.00
CLEAN BOARDS	BOARD H	120.00	131		$8515.00
CUT-LEADS	KIT E	120.00	38		$4750.00
CUT-LEADS	KIT G	120.00	38		$4750.00
Q/C	ASSEMBLY P	120.00	63		$16065.00
Q/C	ASSEMBLY Q	120.00	63		$16065.00
RECV	BOARD F	120.00			
RECV	BOARD H	120.00			
RECV	KIT E	120.00			
RECV	KIT G	120.00			
SHIP	ASSEMBLY P	120.00			
SHIP	ASSEMBLY Q	120.00			
SOLDR	ASSEMBLY P	120.00	59		$14160.00
SOLDR	ASSEMBLY Q	120.00	59		$14160.00

Factory: EXAMPLE SOLDER Menu: Batch Sizes

Fig. 4.7 Required Batch sizes after improving SOLDR

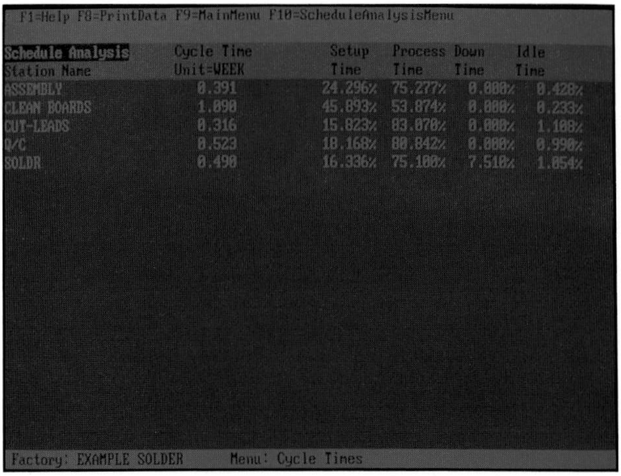

Fig. 4.8 Workstation cycle times after
improving SOLDR

The required lot size at SOLDR will be 59, and the Cycle time will be 0.49, not perfect, but it is enough for now. We aren't satisfied with a 15% failure rate, but we will be repeating products more than twice as often, doubling the rate at which we can do Designed Experiments. This is another example of the connection between rapid cycle time and quality improvement.

Note that correcting the defects at SOLDR also eliminates QC as a problem. It no longer has to re-inspect 30% of the SOLDR output.

What is the next Workstation we should improve? The CLEAN BOARD Workstation has a 1.09 week cycle time and requires a batch size of 131. It should clearly receive the focus of improvement effort. What type of improvement? We will reduce the Setup time using the Four Step Rapid Setup method to be described in Chapter 5. You can then set a rational goal for setup reduction using the Line Analysis program in a "what if" mode as before.

We continue this process in a never ending improvement effort resulting in the reduction of cycle time and batch size required to meet a given customer demand rate. The same results could have been achieved using the trial and error lot size reductions prescribed by Just in Time. For example, by cutting the batch size down to 250, the line would have continued to meet demand. However, cutting the batch size

54

to 125 would have crippled SOLDR, QC, and CLEAN BOARD simultaneously. The line could not meet schedule, and engineering would be overloaded with improvement demands.

The method by which CFM prioritizes improvements is also entirely different from traditional Industrial Engineering practice, which is focused on the reduction of direct labor cost. Referring to any of the top books, such as Barnes, Amerine, Kneibel, etc., one finds many chapters on Time and Motion study or Automation. Traditional practice would thus select the CUT LEAD Workstation as the highest priority for improvement because it has the largest amount of direct labor cost per unit. In virtually all companies, direct labor cost is much lower than manufacturing overhead, scrap, rework and obsolescence; costs which are driven down by reducing the manufacturing cycle time.

CFM does have a means of direct labor cost reduction called Operation time improvement which is discussed in Chapter 5. Line Analysis shows it is generally lower in priority than is quality and setup improvement.

The data shows that there is transport delay between SOLDR and QC. Note that this has a minor impact on overall manufacturing cycle time. If transport delay does become a high priority based on Analysis, we use the Process Flow improvement method described in Chapter 5. This often involves the re-layout of the shop floor into a flow line. This re-layout is usually the last improvement method required.

You can see why most people view Continuous Flow Manufacturing as *the umbrella* program. It encompasses Total Quality Control, Rapid Setup, Statistical Process Control, Quality Circles, Employee Involvement and all other improvement activities in a prioritized fashion by Workstation. This affords a much more focused and effective use of scarce improvement resources.

Range of Application

The batch size calculated by Line Analysis is driven by the schedule of real customer orders. It is thus an electronic version of the mechanical Pull system of Just In Time. It has the further advantage that the Workstation does not need a separate Kanban for each product that a Workstation *may* build. Rather, it only has Kanban containers for those products for which a real demand exists. Thus Continuous Flow Manufacturing is much more flexible allowing a much wider variety of products to be built, in low or high volume. This is in sharp contrast to most applications of Just in Time which are limited to the high volume manufacture of a few products at each Workstation, with a Kanban container for each possible product.

Further, Just In Time proceeds by reducing lot sizes and noting the impact. What about companies that are already manufacturing in small lots? Continuous Flow Manufacturing, using Line Analysis, can prioritize improvements by Workstation cycle time even if the batch size is 1.

Help SortByNumber SortByStation PrintData F9=MainMenu F10=CapacityAnalysis					
Capacity Analysis		Stat Ship	Batch	Scrap	Batch
Station Name	Part Number	Rate/WEEK	Size	Value	Value
ASSEMBLY	ASSEMBLY P	142.86	136		$28560.00
ASSEMBLY	ASSEMBLY Q	142.86	136		$28560.00
CLEAN BOARDS	BOARD F	142.86	200		$13000.00
CLEAN BOARDS	BOARD H	142.86	200		$13000.00
CUT-LEADS	KIT E	142.86	Limit		
CUT-LEADS	KIT G	142.86	Limit		
Q/C	ASSEMBLY P	142.86	406		$123930.00
Q/C	ASSEMBLY Q	142.86	406		$123930.00
RECV	BOARD F	142.86			
RECV	BOARD H	142.86			
RECV	KIT E	142.86			
RECV	KIT G	142.86			
SHIP	ASSEMBLY P	142.86			
SHIP	ASSEMBLY Q	142.86			
SOLDR	ASSEMBLY P	142.86	1883		$451920.00
SOLDR	ASSEMBLY Q	142.86	1883		$451920.00
Factory: EXAMPLE SOLDER	Menu: Batch Sizes				

Fig. 4.9 Production bottleneck has moved
from SOLDR to CUT LEAD

Manufacturing simulation has been the province of specialists who usually have a Masters in Computer Science and rarely visit the factory. The simulation methods in the past have relied on languages such as GPSS or Dynamic simulation models which are very time consuming to build, use and interpret. In these models, you have to *guess* the correct batch size and then see if the queue times increases, by trial and error. In Line Analysis, the correct batch size is calculated at the outset. The goal of Line Analysis is far more practical than is traditional dynamic simulation. We just want to know which Workstations need improvement first, which kind of improvement, how much improvement and the correct batch size and cycle time.

This is much easier to do, and can be understood by Manufacturing supervisors and shop floor personnel who should drive the improvement activity. People with no prior PC background can learn how to use Line Analysis in two days, and spend the third day analyzing their lines. Improvement efforts can only be effective if the Manufacturing supervision participates as full partners. They must therefore be able to use Line Analysis to understand *why* the improvements are necessary.

NOTE: CompeteAmerica™ software is available from the Institute of Business Technology.

Takt Time

In the above discussion, we mentioned that one of the inputs to the Line Analysis program was the firm customer schedule. We will first attempt to 'level' the schedule so that each Operation does about the same amount of work each day. Once the schedule is approximately leveled, it is possible to define the Rhythm of the product line, or the Takt Time. Takt is German for time rhythm, and again, its usage is established.

Let us assume that the customer schedule demands the production of approximately 400 units per day. An 8 hour day consists of 480 minutes less coffee breaks, or a net of 450 minutes. The Takt Time is thus:

$$\text{Takt Time} = \frac{450 \text{ minutes}}{400} = 1.12 \text{ min/unit}$$

The Takt Time is vital, in that it determines the rate at which work must be accomplished at each operation. A related concept is that of the Daily Going Rate. This is simply the available work minutes per day divided by the Takt Time. The Daily Going Rate is the number of units which must be provided per day.

Takt Time thus determines the needed manpower, as well as the required output rate of machines. Because Continuous Flow places fairly steady demands on each work station, the large peak demands which characterize Batch Production are absent. In practice, Continuous Flow plants require far less machine capacity than comparable Batch Production. Reduced machine capacity leads to significantly lower Capital Investment. CFM plants also require far less material handling equipment and space, resulting in the further avoidance of Capital waste. The Takt Time also determines the Kanban quantity. In addition, we may be faced with events over which we have no immediate control. Examples include machine downtime, late supplier delivery, etc. We earlier described the need for a Buffer Kanban to absorb the impact of these problems. The Buffer Kanban quantity is equal to the expected delay time divided by the Takt Time. Eventually, we will solve these problems, as described later, and eliminate the Buffer inventory. Thus, Line Analysis predicts which Operations need extra inventory, and provides a managed transition. This must be contrasted with the Toyota system, where lot size reductions are arbitrary.

In the next Chapter, we shall study some of the tools such as Rapid Setup, Operation Improvement, etc. The Takt Time, thru the Line Analysis program, provides the rational goal for all these efforts. Each Operation must keep up with the Takt Time, nothing more, nothing less.

Cycles of Learning and Lot Size Reduction

We mentioned earlier that, in many cases, Line Analysis shows that Lot sizes can sometimes be reduced by 60% without causing output to fall below demand. In such a case, Lot size should be reduced by 50% immediately, allowing a 10% safety margin. Why should we immediately reduce Lot size? Shouldn't we first start clearing the rocks?

The reason for reducing the Lot size immediately has to do with Cycles of Learning. In our case, clearing the rocks has to do with improving the Setup time or Operation time, etc. for a given product. In the next chapter, we will learn how to reduce these times. The important thing to understand now is that every time you improve, for example the setup design, you will note more opportunities for improvement during setup execution. By reducing Lot size by 50%, you will double the frequency of running the product and doing that setup. This increase in Cycles of Learning is continually accelerated, and makes Manufacturing Engineering far more effective. If, for example, a new setup procedure is designed, but the product is only run once per month, the Engineer will forget some problems and lose momentum. If, however, the product is run every two weeks, he can make faster corrections. The ultimate goal is to be able to economically run some of each product every day. Thus experiments can be planned, approved, executed, analyzed and repeated with maximum velocity of improvement.

Cycle Time and Market Response

We saw in Ford the danger of a narrow product line, and from Sloan the need to offer a very broad product line. In offering a broad product line, it is still necessary to be able to deliver the product within the customer's required lead time. Depending on the product, the customer may expect a one week delivery. With Batch Production, it is necessary to source from a large finished goods inventory or perform Final Assembly from a large sub-assembly inventory. This is caused, of course, by the fact that large lots drive us to infrequent production of each product. In Batch Production, the Cycle Time of the Factory is usually longer than the delivery time required by customers.

In Continuous Flow Manufacturing, small Lot sizes lead to a very fast cycle time. If we are able to build some of each product each day, the Factory Cycle Time is less than the customers lead time. Thus you are able to fill a demand from production, not from inventory.

One also uses the concept of Cycle Time with respect to a Lot. The Cycle Time of a Lot of 100 units is the time to produce all 100 units at a given Operation. Again, the Operation Time is the time to produce one unit.

By reducing the Cycle Time of the Factory, and reducing Lot sizes, one increases inventory turns proportionately. As we saw from the example of Ford, increased inventory turns to 80 per year was his secret in taking $500 of waste out of an $850 car. We also noted the Cycle time of Toyota is less than one week, leading to 70 turns per year and solid profitability. Clearly the Cycle Time is dependent on the product: It takes longer to build a Battleship than a Car. But it can be stated: the competitor with significantly faster inventory turns will have a powerful cost advantage.

Non-Repetitive Manufacturing

Many companies produce such a variety of products that each unit would seem to have no relation to another. Investing Industrial Engineering effort would seem to be a waste, as the product will never be repeated. As we saw in Chapter 3, many companies build a custom product which can be converted to a standard with an overlay of custom features. Still, many products have such a variety of features that, even with some standardization, a very large number of products is built at each Operation. If a Kanban container were provided for each product, a huge number of containers would trap inventory. How can a product with tremendous variation be included in the Pull System?

Computer Kanban

Under the Pull System, each Operation has a container holding the Kanban quantity. When the subsequent Operation removes material, this triggers the effort to build and replace that quantity. A product having large variation would result in a huge number of Kanban containers. This problem is avoided by the method of Computer Kanban. Like the Toyota system, the customer schedule is only given to Final Assembly. Final Assembly takes the firm customer orders Bill of Materials and explodes them down to sub-assemblies. this demand is time shifted based on lead time, and sent to the Operations terminals. Thus Computer Kanban may provide a more precise demand than does the manual Kanban. The danger inherent in computer Kanban is that it will be abused by ordering large batches greater than the Kanban quantity. This danger can be avoided if its consequences are known to all.

There has been an unfortunate and unnecessary debate between the proponents of CFM (JIT) and MRP II. Many CFM advocates condemn MRP, and vice versa. MRP is certainly an excellent yearly material requirements planning method. The precise release of material for delivery should be ideally driven by the need to replenish Kanban. MRP II contains valuable systems such as the Bill of Material Processor (BOMP) which can be used to generate the time shifted Computer Kanban. The primary change is to convert Lot Size quantities from the Economic Lot Size Formula and Marketing Forecast to Kanban quantity, based on Line Analysis. Having levelled the production schedule, the Capacity Planning portion of MRP II is no longer needed. Rather, an improvement effort is directed by Line Analysis to meet Takt Time with ever smaller resources. The talented individuals who have mastered MRP will find many interesting challenges in the conversion of their valuable tools to the needs of Computer Kanban.

The use of the computer to generate Kanban requirements can be extended to other functions. In particular, the computer should also store and display setup instructions. Setup is the source of much waste, particularly in the case of a broad product line. Setup is fully discussed in the next chapter and in Appendix I.

Seasonality

Many industries face a highly seasonal demand for their product. In an effort to level production they believe that they must build a large finished goods inventory to meet peak market demand.

Another strong motivation to build for inventory during slack periods is due to our accounting system, and the high fixed manufacturing Overhead cost of Batch production. Most accounting systems charge Overhead as a percentage of Direct Labor expended on building a product. If high volumes of product are built, the Overhead cost per unit is low, and product margins are preserved on the Income Statement. The unsold product, of course, increases inventory. Because the Manufacturing Overhead is much larger than Direct Labor, there is enormous pressure on Management to "inventory" it rather than to risk a loss. In most companies, Direct Labor is a small component of cost. But we keep Direct Labor fully occupied to avoid large Overhead charges and put the even larger Material cost at risk by building potentially unsaleable product. Further, in Batch production, it is necessary to meet peak demand from finished goods inventory. This is because a Batch Production plant can only ramp up production at a low rate. The way it ramps up production is to increase lot size. This increases cycle time and chokes the plant with Work in Process. This reduces the responsiveness to customer demand, and further increases the exposure to slow moving inventory.

When operating under CFM, these problems are eliminated at the source. Manufacturing Overhead will be comparable to Direct Labor. The ramp-up of production is accomplished by meeting the smaller Takt Time, and Work in Process does not significantly increase. We again use the analogy of the water hose. Increased flow rate does not increase the amount of water in the hose. Further, a smaller Takt Time decreases the cycle time, improving responsiveness to customer demand. The Takt Time can be continuously reduced by applying the CFM methods of Rapid Setup, Defect Prevention, etc. to be discussed in succeeding chapters.

Since Direct Labor *and* Manufacturing Overhead are lower in CFM, there is less motivation to build for inventory during slack periods. What should you do with the extra manpower capacity? The balance of the book provides this answer. Essentially, CFM provides improvement opportunities for every person in the plant. Thus all workers and supervisors will work to eliminate waste, and improve the capability of the plant during the off season. These improvements are much easier to do during slack periods than in full production. It is true that reported costs will slightly increase, but far less than the hidden costs which are a continual year round burden under Batch production.

As CFM implementation proceeds, production for inventory to meet seasonal demands should be gradually diminished.

Range of Application

What are the limitations in the application of Continuous Flow Manufacturing? Many managers think it's a good idea, but believe that "special" problems make it inapplicable to their division. Because CFM was largely developed in the automotive industry, it is wrongly believed to apply to only repetitive assembly tasks, not to process industries. To counter this argument, IBM applied CFM at three entirely different divisions: A Disk Drive plant, a PC Card

Plant, and a Semiconductor process plant. This choice provided a sample of an assembly, a process, and a mixed assembly/process application. In all cases, an approximate 20% reduction in cost and improvements in quality resulted. The conclusion is: CFM applies to all manufacturing, both assembly and process. While JIT principally applied to repetitive manufacturing, CFM (because of Line Analysis) also applies to low volume, small lot as well as high volume production.

Some may question the application of CFM to a job shop. But, as was seen in Chapter 3, analysis may show product similarities in sub-assemblies. This will enable application of CFM. In addition, many of the Rapid Setup and Defect Prevention methods will also be found applicable to Job Shop.

Thorough Implementation

It is essential that all CFM methods be applied, including Mistake Proof Operations, Design of Experiment and Rapid Setup. Line Analysis provides the needed focus by establishing what action must be taken at each Operation, and in what priority. This allows one to focus efforts on the most important task, and to do a thorough job. This assures that the total cost reduction effort will achieve the desired results.

Summary

In this Chapter we traced in outline the development of the flexible version of CFM by Toyota. We discussed the problems of the Toyota method, as well as the advantages of the method based on Line Analysis. We also discussed the concepts of Cycles of Learning and Cycle Time control. Their importance was shown to lie in the velocity with which improvements can be made and customer demand. Cycle Time was shown to be related to Inventory Turns, waste elimination, and lowest cost production.

The primary sources of waste in manufacturing are ultimately due to long setup times, Rework due to Quality Problems, Operation and Transport times. In the next three Chapters, we will learn how to apply the CFM methods to attain the lowest cost, defect free production.

CHAPTER 5

PRODUCT FLEXIBILITY WITH LOW COST

The goal of Continuous Flow Manufacturing is to produce defect free product at the lowest cost. This goal, in turn, requires the economical manufacture of small lots of a broad product line. In the last chapter, we saw that Line Analysis allowed the prediction of which Operation in the Process would first require improvement. Once we have determined which operation is in need of improvement, we can apply one of the CFM improvement methods which were mentioned in the last chapter. The CFM improvement methods are the key to making the actual improvement, and are the subject of this chapter. The ability to reduce setup time by 90%, prevent defects, etc., may appear difficult or impossible. For this reason, most readers find the examples in which these goals have been achieved quite interesting.

We will assume that Line Analysis has been performed, and that we have a prioritized list of operations that are in need of improvement. Line Analysis has also defined the small lot size (regular kanban) that we can use after the improvement activity is successful.

Before we make the lot size reduction, we need to do one or more of the following:

1. Reduce the Setup Time
2. Reduce the Operation time per unit
3. Prevent the Defects, and hence the production time lost to scrap and rework
4. Prevent the machine from failing by better care
5. Reduce the transport time by locating Operations closer together

It is generally best to attack the problem which will give the greatest gain with the least expense. The choice is up to the individual's judgment. Experience shows that, in the majority of cases, setup time and rework/scrap time give the greatest gain. They are improved by the application of intelligence. To reduce operation time may require more expensive capital equipment. To reduce transport time requires the physical disruption of the plant layout. In the example, reduction of Setup Time offers the greatest opportunity, and is the first project which should be investigated.

We will discuss the ways in which setup time, rework time, etc. can be reduced in this and the next few chapters.

Rapid Setup

In our discussion of Henry Ford, we recall his absolute refusal to allow any variety in the Model T. His reasons appeared sound: Variation in the product requires a change in the setup of Operations. The 'inherently' long setup time will interupt Continuous Flow, and lead to production of large batches. Large batches will depress inventory turns. High inventory turns was the key to waste elimination and low cost.

What if the time and cost of setup could be reduced to zero. One could then accept infinite variety in the product at no recurring cost penalty. Clearly this is an ideal which cannot be achieved. This ideal does, however, show the path to simultaneously attaining the low cost of Continuous Flow with the marketing benefits of product variety.

The essential Japanese contribution is their recognition that setup time is not inherently long. Toyota proved, and American companies have confirmed, that virtually all setups can be reduced by 90%. While this is not zero, it is close enough to remove setup time as a practical obstacle to the economic production of small lots.

We will discuss the methods by which setup is reduced later. The question that must occur to the reader is, 'How did we miss such an obvious solution to Ford's problem?' The fact is that most companies, even those in the process industries, build in batches. Once the batch production approach is accepted, setup time is secondary. It is generally 'left up to the workers' initiative,' contrary to Frederick Taylor's admonition. Very little Manufacturing Engineering effort is spent on setup. In fact, in looking at the top five Manufacturing Engineering texts in use, we found a total of only 12 pages devoted to Rapid Setup!

The first effort is to determine if there is some essential reason for the existence of two separate products. Can the customer perceive an advantage? Can the products be re-designed such that B is a minor variation of A? We saw examples of the elimination of un-needed diversity in Chapter 3. If this is successful, we practically eliminate one of the setups. Let us, however, assume that two distinct products are needed.

A four step method has been developed which generally leads to a 90% reduction in setup time without major capital expense. The method organizes the preparation, streamlines the setup, and eliminates adjustments. A few typical examples of setup time reductions include:

	Setup Time (Minutes)	
	Was	Reduced To
Change of Setup of a Milling Machine	45	4
Change of Color in a Dyeing Operation	60	5
Change of Vacuum Mold and Pump Down	2	.16
Change of Spool	20	1
Change of Template in Profiling Lathe	30	.1
Electronic Module Assembly	480	30
Change of Die in a 2700 Ton Press	480	6
Average Reduction = 95%	1249	62

These examples show that the Four Step Method is of a general nature. It applies to all chemical, physical, assembly and machine tool Operations.

Four Step Method

Step 1. *Separate the Setup into two portions:*
External Setup: Changes that can be done while the Operation is producing.
Internal Setup: Changes which require the Operation to be shut down.

Step 2. *Convert Internal Setup to External Setup*

Step 3. *Streamline Internal*

Step 4. *Eliminate Adjustments*

Let us illustrate the method with the first example. This particular milling machine has a 10 tool spindle and can change tools in 1.2 seconds. It operates under Numerical Control. The items of work to be drilled or milled are clamped to its bed. Before improvement, the change of setup was done as follows: When the last good part of the run was finished, the machine was shut down. The Operator removed the completed work from the bed, removed and cleaned the tools. The operator then read the next work order and gathered the necessary tooling from the tool crib (distance: 75 feet). Each tool in the 10 tool spindle was changed. The Operator then went to the stockroom to requisition material for that part (distance: 100 feet). The Operator clamped the material to the bed, checked the alignment, and started the machine. Total elapsed time was 45 minutes. Run time of the machine to complete the lot was 20 minutes. The setup was improved as follows:

Step 1: Separate Internal Setup from External Setup

The present setup procedure is entirely internal, because the machine is shut down during the whole period. However, some of the setup could be performed while the machine is running, which would make them External Setup. In particular, the tools and materials could be gathered prior to shutdown.

Step 2: Convert Internal Setup to External Setup

An auxiliary bed and tool spindle can be purchased for the machine for less than 5% of the machine's cost. The beds will be placed on rails so either can slide under the tool spindle. This will allow the work for the next run to be clamped to the bed externally, while the machine is running. Tools for the next run can be inserted into the chucks of the auxilliary spindle while the machine is running. The spindle is then moved into position on a slide, when the machine is shut down.

Step 3: Streamline Internal Setup

The spindle is held in place by a check pin and four bolts. Each bolt requires 15 turns. The bolts were replaced by heavy duty CAM levers. This reduces spindle replacement time by 2 minutes.

Step 4: *Eliminates Adjustments:*

It is important that the center of the bed be directly under the "home" position of the milling head. This eliminates the need to make trial cuts and adjustments of bed position. The bed is centered by a notch in the rail thru which a locking handle is inserted.

As the examples above show, the method can be applied to chemical, process, molding, etc. applications as well as machine tools.

Rapid Setup. This 2700 ton United States Industries press normally takes 6 hours to change the setup. Using the four step method, Nissan reduced the setup time to 6 minutes. The lot size of each door type has been reduced from 3840 to 175, a 95% inventory reduction!

The details of how setup time reduction was achieved in all the applications in the table is given in Appendix I. At this point, the important conclusion to draw is that Setup time and cost can be reduced by 90% with little capital equipment expense. The reader of Appendix I will find that the mere act of organizing the effort (Step 1) will reduce setup time by 50%.

Operation Improvement

The Operation Time is defined as the time needed to build each unit. The essential requirement is that the Operation Time per unit be sufficient to keep up with the Takt time.

The first effort in reducing the Operation Time per unit is to eliminate wasted human labor. A Four Step Method, very similar to that employed in Rapid Setup, is used to stream line the human effort. The details of the method are contained in Appendix I. Recall from the examples of Chapters 2 and 3 that 50% reduction in Operation time are possible by often modest efforts (eg. Ford piston assembly, IPM relay assembly.)

Engineers often believe that improving Operating Time requires capital equipment with faster production rates. This is generally an expensive investment. Before such a step is taken, one should carefully evaluate the possibility of Reduced Setup, Rework, etc. In our example, a 90% reduction in the times other than Operation time would result in an additional 193 minutes of Operating Time per day. This would increase production capacity by more than 70% with no improvement in work methods or capital equipment production rates. Additional production capacity could be secured by applying the Four Step Method to the Operation eliminating wasted human motion and effort.

In the Batch production environment, the principle method of productivity improvement is through faster, more expensive machines. In Continuous Flow, the principle method of obtaining productivity improvement is through waste elimination. Automation and Robotics do have a valid role to play, but only after a thorough waste elimination effort.

A word must be said about economies of scale and learning curves. We have all heard the theory that, as the Batch size increases (or the production run lengthens), the worker "learns" the Operation, and the cost falls. In Batch production, this phenomena is actually observed for two reasons. First, the cost includes the long setup time. As Batch size increases, the setup cost per unit falls. The learning of the worker is due to increased proficiency which is acquired through repetition. This increased proficiency is primarily due to the fact that inadequate work instructions or training are in place. In short, once the setup time has been reduced 90%, and proper work instructions and training are in place, economies of scale or "learning" are of little importance. Thus small lot production is as labor efficient as large lot production.

Machine Repair Downtime: **Preventive Maintenance**

Unscheduled machine downtime is dangerous because its duration is unpredictable. The majority of equipment downtime is caused by poor lubrication, calibration drift, defective drive belts, or other simple factors. The Operator knows the machine better than anyone, and can often predict a problem based on experience. The routine maintenance of the equipment can and should be performed by workers. This will free Maintenance to focus their attack on chronic problems. Another factor related to preventive maintenance is housekeeping. The worker must be trained to keep all machines and tools clean and in good order. By keeping all bearings wiped clean, one can detect oil leakage or bushing shavings. Thus an early sign of problems may be detected and corrected.

Transport Time: **Process Flow Improvement**

Transportation time is the time from the production of the last good part of a lot to the delivery of the last good part to the next Operation. It includes waiting time, pickup delays, etc.

As has been previously discussed, the transportation time between Operations is usually the least important factor affecting lot size. When this does become a problem, we must:

• *Re-layout the Process to achieve physical continuous flow of the product.*

- *If re-layout is impossible or too expensive, use buffer Kanban, i.e., extra controlled inventory to compensate for Transportation time.*

Operations should ideally be positioned an arms length away. It is much better to eliminate transportation than to automate it. To automate transportation with expensive capital equipment is to replace one waste with a bigger one. Half the roller conveyors in a plant are used as expensive storage racks for materials, i.e., their need was generated by Batch production.

Process Flow Improvement. The line has been laid out for Continuous Flow. Operators are close enough to hand-off completed work, check for defects of previous workers, and assist one another. Their material is stored in replaceable bins, allowing for a Rapid Setup of the Operation for a different product. Note that lights above the operation allow the worker to signal problems.

In laying out a physical flow line, the 'U' shape has been found very successful. The 'U' shape reduces walking time between operations by half. This brings workers closer together, makes it more of a family or 'team,' and facilitate cross training. Cross training is very valuable because it makes the line less susceptible to illness, and facilitates Line Balancing and response to changes in production rates. If you can't exactly balance the work at each operation, you can time share the workers at more than one operation. Cross training leads to a form of job enrichment for the worker, and also increases the number of suggestions and work from the Problem Solving Teams, to be discussed later and in Chapter 10.

Summary:

In this chapter, we have shown how the CFM tools are effective in allowing the economical production of small lots at low cost. Thus the goal of achieving Henry Ford's low cost *with* product variety is within our grasp. There is one factor which has not yet been discussed, Defects. Defects cause lost productivity, rework, scrap and many thus be a Bottleneck, or 'rock' just like long setup. But defects also cause unhappy customers and loss of market share. Because of the crucial impact of quality, a special discussion follows in the next two chapters.

CHAPTER 6

QUALITY WITH LOW COST

In the last chapter we learned that our drive to become cost competitive on a worldwide basis was dependent on an adaptation of Ford's Continuous Flow Production Method. We briefly introduced the major tools used in its implementation.

One of the tools is particularly important because it decisively influences productivity, profitability and market share. This is the Quality element, whose impact is not at all obvious, and hence is deserving of special attention. Thus far, our only concern with Quality was a result of our Line Analysis effort. It takes just as long to build a bad part as a good one. Thus defective parts cause an effective loss of productive capacity. A significant portion of Operation time may be spent building scrap parts or reworking defectives. Line Analysis will show this as a "Pinch Point" or rock at the offending Operation. One American manufacturer experiences a 35% reject rate on machined drive train components. A competitor experiences a 12% reject rate. All things being equal, the company with the higher defect rate must have 35% more production capacity. (It's an inverse relation) This is a severe competitive disadvantage, and one which surprises most people. Before we proceed, a few definitions relating to quality are helpful.

All goods and services are produced in various grades or levels of quality. These variations in grades or levels of quality are intentional, and, consequently, the appropriate terms is *Quality of Design.* For example, all automobiles have as their basic objective providing safe transportation for the consumer. However, automobiles differ with respect to size, appointments, appearance, and performance. A Mercedes Benz has a higher Quality of Design than a Volkswagen. As an example, the Mercedes Benz engine parts are balanced to avoid engine vibration. The VW uses ordinary forgings; exceptionally low engine vibration is not a VW design goal. These differences are the result of international and deliberate design differences between the automobiles.

73

Quality of Conformance is how well the product produced by Manufacturing actually meets the requirements of the design. A Mercedes Benz whose engine vibrates because of mismatched parts in assembly has poor quality of conformance. A VW Beetle that runs reliably has a high quality of conformance, even though it may be noisy. Quality of Conformance is influenced by a number of factors, including the choice and control of manufacturing processes, the training and supervision of the work force, and the type of quality system employed by the manufacturer.

There is considerable confusion in our society about quality. The term is often used without making clear whether we are talking about Quality of Design or Quality of Conformance. To achieve Quality of Design requires conscious decisions during the product or process design stage. To achieve Quality of Conformance requires that the manufacturing process itself must be designed with defect prevention and continuous reduction of variation as integral elements. Quality of Design will be discussed in the chapter on Corporate Strategy. This and the next chapter will discuss Quality of Conformance.

Quality and Customer Preference

Quality is not just a marginal factor in market penetration, it is a life-or-death matter. An example of this is to be found in the Video Cassette Recorder (VCR) market. The VCR is a complex product from both an electronic and mechanical standpoint. The first units for home use were produced in Europe by Phillips and Grundig. In the early days, no product gave appliance stores more trouble than the VCR. Then the Japanese products arrived in Europe, and were virtually trouble-free. They solved the quality of conformance problem, building a defect free product. What had been a troublesome, small market became a huge, dynamic market of happy retailers and satisfied customers. Phillips and Grundig were driven from their own market, which today is more than 90% Japanese.

As another example, let's look at the impact of Japanese automobile manufacturing on the U.S. automobile market. Over the past 15 years, Japanese companies have captured approximately 35% of the market. Prior to the imposition of U.S. "Restraints" on Japanese imports, their penetration of the California market exceeded 50%. The most important factor cited in consumer preferences for Japanese cars is superior Quality.

Impact of Product Complexity on Quality and Cost

As products grow in complexity, the need for quality at every step of design and manufacturing increases. In the Introduction, we considered the example of one of the most complex of all industrial products, the 256K RAM. The much higher yield of good product allows the Japanese to dominate this market.

How have the Japanese achieved these higher yields and lower costs? In this case, by the use of better process control and capability improvement techniques by which defects are prevented and process variability continually reduced. These techniques are the subject of the next chapter. What concerns us now is the Philosophy of Prevention. In a complex product, quality must be checked at every step, and every defect must trigger a continuous effort at prevention and process improvement.

Consider a product which requires 100 steps in its manufacture. If, on the average, you have a 95% yield at each step, you will get less than 1% good product. If you improve each step of the process to 99% yield, you will get 36% good product, at the same cost! A small improvement in yield per step gives a tremendous reduction in the cost per good unit. The effects of "Defect Prevention at Each Step" is overwhelming, and leads to product costs which make the American Semi-conductor industry uncompetitive. U.S. chip makers posted Operating Losses over $1 billion in 1986. Over the last two years, the Semi-conductor industry laid off 65,000 workers. In 1982, America had 49% of the worldwide integrated circuit market, compared to 26% for Japan. At the end of 1986, Japan had 38%, versus 35% for the U.S. the fact that the total electronics market is "down" does not account for a 14% drop in market share.

We will return to this theme in the next chapter and show how defect prevention and continuous improvement can be implemented.

Quality and the Product Development Cycle

Since 1960, the complexity of all products, from automobiles to ovens has increased. All of these "old" products now contain new features based on sophisticated electro-mechanical systems.

Microwave ovens, dishwashers, cameras, stereos and hundreds of other products are dependent on sophisticated electronics. In addition, a host of new products including home computers, video cassette recorders, office copiers, etc. are even more sophisticated. Nor has the impact of new technology upon products been limited to electronics. The last 20 years has seen an explosion of technology in virtually every field including metallurgy, ceramics, composite materials, bio-technology, chemical and pharmaceutical sciences. The pace of materials technology will rapidly accelerate as entirely new properties are synthesized based on knowledge at the structure-of-matter level. We will soon have "designer" materials.[2] The basic problem faced by industry impacted by rapid technological change is to develop and produce competitive product in a timely manner. In this environment, it is easy to pay too little attention to achieving quality and low cost during the design, development and manufacturing phases.

As the complexity of modern products has increased, the number of steps in engineering and manufacturing also increased. Each step puts both quality and cost at risk. As the technology employed is rapidly changing, the manufacturer, to an increasing degree, is further increasing the risk by employing new components, new materials and new processes. The probability of delivering a low-quality high-cost product to the customer is thus increased. This probability becomes a near certainty when new products are developed by Design Engineering without early Manufacturing Engineering involvement. Massive Engineering Change Orders (ECO) result from first attempts at production. Engineering attention is totally overcommitted to getting these problems solved, and is diverted from developing defect free or cost effective manufacturing methods. Thus a terrible price is paid to generate and implement the ECO. Inadequate attention is paid to cost, the result of which is a high cost product whose quality of conformance and hence reliability are in dire jeopardy. In the chapter on Corporate Strategy, we will make specific recommendations to avoid this all too common problem. In essence, we recommend that a Product Delivery Team including Development, Manufacturing and Marketing be created at the outset of the development effort. In this way the Assembly, process and defect prevention methods can be developed along with the product, and ECO waste and high product cost prevented.

We have seen the impact of coming up second best in quality in the marketplace. In automobiles, VCR's, television, optics, machine tools, and a host of other products, the consumer rewards the high quality producer with nearly the whole market! But how does quality affect cost and productivity? Doesn't high quality mean high cost? If we push quality, won't production go down and cost go up?

The Quality-Productivity-Profitability Link

Consider the manufacture of a mechanical component. The parts are manufactured in a machining process at a rate of approximately 100 parts per hour at a cost of $20 per part. For various reasons, the process is operating at a yield of 65% (that is, about 35% of the output is non-conforming). The process fallout can be classified as either re-work or scrap. About 15% of the output can be re-worked into acceptable product and the remaining 20% must be scrapped. Parts that can be re-worked incur an additional processing charge of $4.00. The time required to rework a part is the same as the time to initially machine a unit, but also requires an additional $4.00 microfinish, inspection and test charge. Only 100 parts can be processed per hour, including those reworked. Thus 87 new parts are processed of which 57 are good, 13 parts are reworked, and 17 are scrapped. Therefore, the manufacturing cost for a good part produced is:

$$\text{Cost} = \frac{87(\$20) + 13(\$4)}{70} = \$25.60$$

Note that the total yield from this process after re-work is 70 parts per hour. The defective parts were eliminated by inspection and test, but the cost of material, labor, and overhead of the scrap units was already expended.

A Manufacturing engineering study of this process reveals that the source of the extremely high fallout level is excessive tool chatter.

Industrial Engineering implements a new feed-speed-coolant setup that reduces the defect from 35% to 12% preventing 23% of the failures. Now only about 5% of the process output requires re-work and 7% is scrapped. After the process improvement program is implemented, the manufacturing cost per good part produced is:

$$\text{Cost} = \frac{95(\$20) + 5(\$4.00)}{88} = \$21.81$$

Installing process improvement in this manufacturing system results in a 15% reduction in manufacturing costs. Furthermore, productivity is up by 26%; 88 good parts are produced each hour as opposed to 70 good parts previously. This amounts to an increase in production capacity of 26% without any additional investment in equipment, work force, or overhead. This is an example of how inspection and test may reject defects, but only prevention can lower cost and improve productivity.

Investment in quality improvement will usually cause the "bottom line" to grow faster than any othe single investment alternative. Suppose you invest $100,000 in preventing defects. In the next chapter, you will learn how such an investment in prevention can result in at least $1,000,000 in future cost savings. If half of this savings flows to the bottom line, then the addition of profit is $500,000 annually. Suppose that the after tax contribution of this product is 10% of the selling price. To realize $500,000 additional profit through increased sales activity you would have to sell $5,000,000 worth of additional product. Could you do that with a $100,000 investment? Not in most business! From this simple example we see that high quality requires prevention, a usually small one time investment in Manufacturing Engineering. It then yields an ongoing payback in lower cost and higher productivity. This concept is so vital, and so misunderstood, that it appears on Page 1 of Dr. Deming's famous book on quality. Dr. Deming is the originator of a 14 point philosophy of quality in business which had a major impact on Japanese thinking.

The Cost of Quality

The quality of your product has a cost, just like material cost and labor cost. This cost of quality can be divided into four components:

1. Prevention: the cost of preventing defects.

2. Appraisal: the cost of inspections, test and audit.

3. Internal Failure: the cost of scrap, rework, repair, lost productivity, etc. for the defects you find prior to shipment to the customer.

4. External Failure: the cost of defects your customer finds or which escape to the field, including warrant costs, repairing, replacements, field servicing, engineering changes, good will, lost reputation, and lost orders.

The cost of correcting a defect rises rapidly as it progresses undetected through the manufacturing cycle and on to the customer. These are large costs in most companies; as large as 20 to 30 percent of total sales. The key strategy in managing quality cost is to invest in prevention.

The usefulness of investing in quality improvement through prevention, like all Manufacturing Engineering effort, stems from leverage effects; dollars invested in prevention are one-time costs, but have a high permanent pay-off in reducing dollars incurred in internal and external failures. Dollars spent on internal and external failure are recurring, and have no permanent benefit.

We have seen graphic examples of the impact of high quality of conformance on sales. The Japanese VCR achieved a higher quality of conformance than did Phillips and Grundig. What was the return? A billion dollar industry! As we shall subsequently see, the prevention techniques used in achieving quality are not expensive. The methods depend on straightforward engineering, and are not the result of cultural differences or motivational methods. They result in high productivity and low cost which more than pays the implementation cost. In addition, prevention eliminates the far larger costs of internal and external failure, and loss of market share.

We have described the increasing complexity and the rapid technological change in modern products. By focusing management and engineering skills on a prevention effort, the cost of defectives can be eliminated. No matter how complex the product, no matter how many steps are involved, we can eliminate defects by installing defect prevention at every step.

At present, many Western companies allocate less than 5% of their quality costs to prevention. This may have been adequate for the realtively simple products sold to the unsophisticated consumers of the past, but it no longer suffices in todays worldwide competitive environment. The next chapter shows how 100% defect prevention can be achieved by economical and practical means.

Summary

We discussed examples of marketplace success and failure due to high Quality of Conformance. The increasing complexity of modern products requires a program to prevent defect re-occurrence. An example demonstrated that defect prevention yields high quality at low cost. Inspection and test alone may yield high quality but at high cost. The next chapter will describe the specific tools which can prevent defects 100% of the time.

---

[1]Time; Oct 27, 1986, Pg. 72
[2]Scientific American, October, 1986
[3]Deming, W. E. "Quality, Productivity and Competitive Position," Cambridge: MIT, 1982

CHAPTER 7

PREVENTION OF DEFECTS

We now understand the imperative need for defect prevention at every step of the manufacturing process. But how can you prevent defects 100% of the time? Isn't this an impossible goal? Wouldn't perfect quality increase cost?

In this chapter we are going to show **how** defects can be 100% prevented, with lower, not higher quality costs. We will first discuss the means to prevent defects caused by workers and machines, then discuss defect prevention in processes.

Mistake Proof Operations (MPO)

Some of the most vexing errors are those in which a worker's mistake is covered up by his later work. As an example, consider Fig. 7.1A. The worker is performing one step in automobile distributor assembly. His job is to first install an electronic module, and then put on the distributor cap. If he forgets to install the module, but instead puts on the cap, we have a defect. The lack of a module will not be noticeable by subsequent workers or Quality Control, and will progress through the line until it is completely assembled and ready for test. At that point, the failure will be detected, and all assembly labor lost, plus rework and diagnostic cost. Production output is diminished and inventory turns is depressed. This defect actually occurred in up to 3% of the product.

Fig. 7.1A: Traditional Assembly

How can we be sure that the module is inserted before the cap is put on? Should we lecture the worker, or automate the function? Let's assume we can only spend $500 to prevent the defect from ever recurring. Automation is too expensive and is thus eliminated. Rather, we will re-design the Operation for Mistake Proof Operations (MPO). Refer to Fig. 7.1B. We place a light source and photoelectric switch shutter on a magazine of caps. When the worker reaches for a module, his hand interrupts the light beam. This causes the photoelectric switch to operate the electric shutter, dropping one cap. If he forgets to first reach for a module, he can't get a cap. Thus the defect is prevented. This system has been in operation for two years, with no defects.

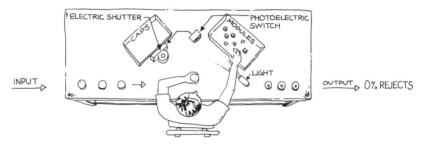

Fig. 7.1B: Mistake Proof Operations

One of the authors' 16 year old son, Michael George Jr., was concerned that the worker might not put the module in. He recommends positioning the distributor on a jig, with a laser directed at the module, and a photoelectric switch positioned at the reflected angle from the module. This is an even more foolproof system. Once engineers begin the program, every defect will become an interesting challenge to build an inexpensive MPO to catch it. Design and development Engineers, Technicians & workers will all enjoy this beneficial work.

- *'Handedness' Mistake Proof Operation:* Virtually every production operation must build parts whose sole difference is that they are left or right handed. The hole patterns are mirror images, so if a left handed panel is bent as a right handed panel, it must be scrapped.
  The handedness MPO consists of two limit switches, which poke through the unique left and right hand mounting holes.

If you are set up for the right hand holes, and put on a left hand panel, it will press on the switch, sound a buzzer, and remove power from the machine so that the 'start' button won't work.

- *Filling a Container:* Frequently an Operator must fill a container with a liquid or gas. For example, in charging a refrigerator compressor, the Operator must hold the valve on for a sufficient time. An undercharged refrigerator leads to a start up warranty call from the manufacturer. The explanation was that the Operator had not held the valve open a sufficient time. The solution is to replace the all manual valve with a valve controlled by time and a pressure transducer. Once the Operator switches the valve on it will always fill the correct amount before it turns off.

- *Cut Off Operation:* In many production operations, metal stock must be cut to a desired length. The metal stock is fed into a shear until it reaches the backstop. The blade is then actuated. There is danger that the stock may bounce away from the backstop, leading to variation in length. The problem exists in both manual and automatic feed and cutoff machines. The solution is to electrically insulate the backstop from the machine. The backstop is connected to a small positive DC voltage, the machine to a small negative. The current path flows thru the machine's turn on relay using an anti-bounce circuit. Unless the metal stock is maintained in contact with the backstop, no current will flow, and the shear will not operate. This prevents any variation in length.

- *Welding:* In the manual welding of parts to a chassis, the Operator may frequently forget to make one of the welds. This can be a serious matter, jeopardizing the strength, function and safety of the product. How can we be sure that the proper number of welds are made? A simple attack is to install a computer on the welding gun current, connected to a relay clamp on the work. The counter counts the number of current pulses, and compares it to the required number. If the Operator forgets a weld, the counter will not release the relay, and the work cannot be moved. It is also possible to measure the current duration of each weld to verify weld strength.

The majority of Operator errors can be attacked using Mistake Proof Operations methods, limited only by our imagination. All that is required is the attitude and determination to build prevention mechanisms, and a small amount of money. The goal is to make a simple, hence cheap and reliable, prevention mechanism. As a rule, prevention mechanisms should return ten times their cost the first year in terms of the reduced cost of rework, scrap, warranty, and increased productivity. The Defect Prevention mechanism should be designed as a permanent fixture if possible. Alternatively, it should be installed as part of the External Setup.

Self Checking Machines

Thus far, we have discussed the application of Mistake Proof Operations to prevent defects due to human error. The same methods apply to machines. Let us take a very simple example to illustrate the method. Assume that we have an automatic machine whose job is to stamp out discs, and grind them to a thickness of 0.2 inches, plus or minus 0.010 inches. (Fig. 7.2) It is possible that the grinding operation may go out of tolerance, producing parts which are too thick or too thin. We could use a human inspector to occasionally take a sample. The human inspector may get bored or fatigued, and miss a few parts. Human inspection is thus an expensive and uncertain method. We may end up with a large number of rejects. Let us replace the human inspector with a pair of gates. Each 'gate' will consist of a flat steel bar suspended above a flat inclined steel plate. The first gate will be suspended 0.210 inches above the plate. Any disc thicker than this will be blocked, and slide off into a small defect box, tripping an alarm. All discs thinner than 0.210 will pass under the first gate and will then encounter the second 'gate.' The second gate is suspended 0.190 inches above the plate. Any discs thinner than 0.190 inches will pass under the second gate and trip an alarm. The good discs will be blocked by the second gate and slide off into a production bin. Any disc thinner than 0.190 will pass under the second gate, fall into the thin reject bin and trip an alarm.

Clearly we have 100% inspection. Clearly we have no inspector to suffer fatigue. The only cost is to invest a little Manufacturing Engineering time setting up the inclined plate and gates. Assuming the stamping and grinding operations were performed by linked automatic machines, you have the jeopardy of building many defects quickly. One could connect a relay from the reject sensors to the machine's circuit breakers, turning them off (shunt trip). Thus, at most only one or a few parts will be made in error, but none will be passed on to the next stage of production. This simple example illustrates the philosophy of Defect Prevention.

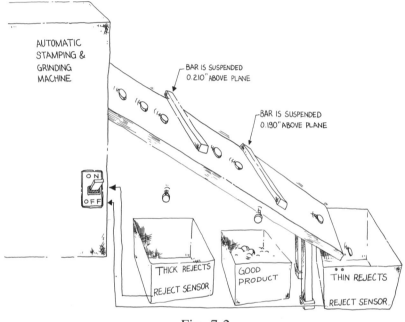

AUTOMATIC STAMPING & GRINDING MACHINE

BAR IS SUSPENDED 0.210" ABOVE PLANE

BAR IS SUSPENDED 0.190" ABOVE PLANE

ON
OFF

THICK REJECTS
REJECT SENSOR

GOOD PRODUCT

THIN REJECTS
REJECT SENSOR

Fig. 7.2

To obtain more precision, gauging sensors can be used, or laser interferometers, etc. The philosophy is the same: an independent gauging mechanism is able to shut the machine down to prevent defects.

In this example, we have eliminated the rejects, eliminated the rework, eliminated the human inspector. In fact, we have eliminated waste. Inspection is one-at-a-time at the source of error, not in a huge lot at a remote QC station, where scrap or rework is the only 'solution.'

This simple example can be refined in both tolerance and capability, but illustrates the philosophy of prevention as applied to machines.

Once a Mistake Proof Operation method is yielding defect free parts, Quality Control focus should change. Quality Control's new job is to verify that the MPO method is in use and in calibration. QC can work up new defect prevention methods, and tackle supplier problems with better tools. QC thus becomes a high leverage profit generator, rather than solely a non-value add inspection function.

Successive Checks

The majority of assembly errors are susceptible to detection and correction by a simple and inexpensive Mistake Proof Operation method. Still, some errors may not be susceptible to MPO. In electronic printed circuit card assembly, most components can only be inserted one way. Axial lead diodes, however, are symmetrical, and can be inserted backwards. Most manufacturers put the diode direction on the PC board silkscreen, but assembly errors will still occur.

By using the maximum number of MPO, we will reduce the number of possible errors and, consequently, the number of things we must look at. We can then focus our worker training on those remaining areas, employ visual aids, etc. Still, we have the old problem of the subjectivity of the worker who builds the assembly not finding his own errors.

How can we keep the responsibility for quality at the source, i.e., in the hands of the workers, and not lose objectivity? By the technique of Successive Checks. Basically, each worker will perform a few checks on errors frequently made by the preceding workers. Essentially this is a mini incoming inspection, which can be facilitated with visual aids, templates, jigs and fixtures. In the case of the diode, we would provide a template with cut outs where the common errors occur. At the edge of the template cutouts, we would draw the proper diode directions. This template would be supplied to both the worker who installed the diode, as well as the subsequent worker. Errors which are very prevalent may trigger the need for Manufacturing Engineering to investigate to see if the design should be changed, or rethink the possibility of an MPO. Failing this, the offending error may be subjected to a second Successive Check by the next Operation.

Any error detected by a worker will be immediately carried back to the source worker, providing immediate feedback and stopping any more errors. Successive Checks, though not as strong as Mistake Proof Operations, retain the needed objectivity.

What About Lot Sampling:

Many companies still accept or reject lots by testing a small sample, and passing the whole lot if the sample is good. The problem with this method is that it is possible that some portion of the lot is defective. In the older books,[1] Sampling inspection was justified as being as good as a 100% inspection. The argument was made that a human inspector will become bored and fatigued inspecting 1000 parts. Studies showed that inspector error rates as high as 30% were common. Thus, it was argued, a very conscientious inspection of a small sample can be as effective, and far less costly, than a 100% inspection. Notice that our Defect Prevention methods depend on machines or templates, not human inspectors. These Mistake Proof Operation Methods provide a 100% inspection but eliminate the human fatigue factor, the repetitive cost, and the possibility of passing defects.

Further, because of increasing product complexity, we cannot tolerate any defects. Thus lot sampling *should not be used* for lot acceptance. In-process sampling is, however, valuable to determine if the process is under control. This is discussed later in the section on Statistical Process Control.

Design For Manufacture (DFM)

We have discussed how Mistake-Proof Assembly and Successive Checks prevent errors form becoming defects. There is yet a third tool: Design for Manufacture.

You will recall the problem of distributor assembly and the Mistake Proof Operations which made it more probable that the module was inserted before the cap was put on. What if we so designed the cap so that it could not be attached unless the module were in place. Referring back to the problem of the diodes, one could redesign the PC Board to use Dual In-Line rather than Axial lead components. The Dual In-Line carriers are indexed for machine insertion, preventing the error.

Instead of waiting for defects to occur, we try to anticipate opera-

87

tion problems at the design state. Those defects which slip past us can be attacked with MPO and Successive Checks. Later on, each problem which occasioned Mistake Proof Operations for Successive Check can be examined as a candidate for Design for Manufacture effort. This example highlights the need for cooperation between Manufacturing and Engineering. Engineering must receive training in Defect Prevention so that they can make the Design for Manufacture effort possible. The involvement of Design and Manufacturing should ideally begin at the outset of development. In this way, Manufacturing can help guide the design toward processes and methods which are defect free.

The crucial nature of the early involvement of Design and Manufacturing engineers can be appreciated by an example from the semi-conductor industry. Mostek was the early leader in producing both 4K and 16K Random Access Memory (RAM) chips. The next step was clearly a 64K RAM. The Japanese chose to use the proven high yield Mostek design as their basis. Manufacturing considerations were paramount in determining the business strategy. they began shipping product in 1981.

Texas Instruments chose a more complex design than that used in the Mostek 16K RAM. The TI chip also had higher density, ie., more chips per slice. Intel chose an even higher density advanced design. National used a very complex new process to reduce circuit size. Although manufacturing and cost considerations were important, Design Engineering and Marketing considerations were paramount in determining business strategy. All of these American firms had extreme difficulties with new and untried processes. They were not factors in the market until 1983, two years after Japanese entry. By this time, Japanese yields were so high, and costs were so low, that the American firms had a very difficult time competing. The 'Window of Opportunity' to make a profit was closing. The Japanese retained over 50% of the U.S. market.

This example is not unique to the semi-conductor industry. Failure to involve manufacturing as an equal in business strategy has in fact caused whole factories to be unproductive for an extended period. In this case, a profit opportunity was irretrievably lost. This loss set the stage for a weak U.S. performance in the next product generation, the 256K RAM, discussed in the Introduction.

88

Statistical Process Control and Capability Improvement

We have developed several powerful defect prevention methods including Mistake Proof Operations, Successive Checks, etc. This will allow one to focus effort on those operations where these methods do not apply. How do you *prevent* defects in a process; i.e., an Operation in which the Defects are not caused by an Operator? A few examples will illustrate the problem.

Let us assume we are casting parts from an alloy which consists of six metals. If the tensile strength fails to meet specification, what do you do? If you are cracking a crude petroleum feedstock, how do you get the most good product out of the process, given variation in the input crude, catalyst flow, and a host of other variables? If you are fabricating semi-conductor devices, how do you optimize yield? If a wave solder machine is generating bad solder joints, how do you correct the problem?

The first step is to use the methods of Statistical Process Control to determine if the process is under control. We first take samples of the output, eg. the tensile strength of the alloy in our first example. We calculate the average value, and the range from highest to lowest value. We plot the average value and range on Conrtol Charts and compare them to statistical control limits. So long as the points are within the limit points and are randomly located around the desired average, we say the process is *under control*. This means that to improve the process, we must change the process itself. When points go outside the control limits, the process is out-of-control. Then we should look for *assignable causes*, conditions such as operator error, defective material to be corrected. More details of Statistical Process Control are contained in Appendix II for the interested reader.

All processes have a certain amount of variability in their output. Figure 7.3A shows the tensile strength of an alloy casting used in a jet engine. Most of the product falls above the desired value, but a few are below strength limit and hence are defects. We describe this problem by saying that the Capability of the Process is inadequate to prevent defects. How can we improve the Capability of the process to prevent defects?

89

Statistically Designed Experiments:

Designed Experiments are a method of preventing defects from a process which are not caused by operator error.

The problem then, is to find out which of the myriad possible variables actually affect the tensile strength. The process of casting a jet engine alloy consists of using six different metals with a choice of two heat treat methods. The major influence on tensile strength is the percentage composition of the various metals, and the type of heat treat chosen. The traditional approach is to vary one parameter while holding the others constant. The hope is that the tensile strength will increase due to a change in one of the variables. This method neglects the fact that the tensile strength may depend on the *interaction* of two or more variables. To catch these interactions, one must allow simultaneous variation of all parameters, We have six metals and a heat treat. If each variable takes on two values, we must run a total of 128 tests, to catch all the interactions.

Using the technique known as Design of Experiment[3], we can get all the important data with just 16 tests. Designed Experiments allow us to find those parameters which improve tensile strength. One possibility is to determine those changes in percentage, and those interactions, which increase tensile strength. One then makes those corrections, and drives the mean value of tensile strength higher, Fig. 7.3B. Shifting the mean value higher may, however, adversely influence some other parameter. An alternate method is to reduce the variability in the process. This is achieved by determining which changes in variables increase the variation, and which decrease variation in tensile strength. One then makes appropriate corrections to reduce variation, Fig. 7.3C. This process is greatly aided by the technique of Residuals. It allows one to obtain the necessary information from the original 16 tests.

Processes should be brought under control and yield maximized during the Development phase by a cooperative Designed Experiment effort involving Manufacturing and Engineering. Production processes generally differ from the lab process, and additional Designed Experiments should be done *in production.* Again, one would make small variations in each lot, such that we would not spoil the output. Each lot thus provides additional data to our 16 test set, allowing us to continually improve the process. One can again

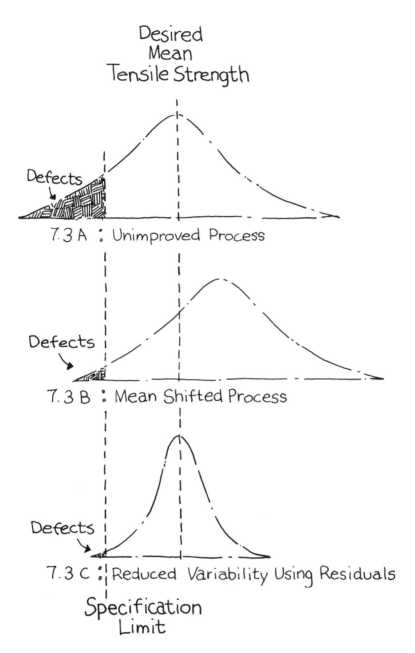

Desired
Mean
Tensile Strength

Defects

7.3 A : Unimproved Process

Defects

7.3 B : Mean Shifted Process

Defects

7.3 C : Reduced Variability Using Residuals

Specification
Limit

Fig. 7.3: Process Defect Prevention using Designed Experiment

see the advantage of small lot sizes which are frequently run, in that we increase the rate of improvement. The method is entirely general, and can be applied to any number of variables in any process.

Quality Circles

The concept of Quality Circles is based on the idea that, if workers generate defects, they must be involved in the prevention effort. One must first have the engineering capability to implement Defect Prevention Methods already discussed. Otherwise, defects will continue to occur, and workers will be de-motivated by the problem. Assuming such a capability exists, workers can then provide a very valuable input. Examples include:

1. Identification of the most frequent quality problems.
2. Suggestions for better methods for setup and operations.
3. Assistance in cross training other operators.
4. Routine preventive maintenance and housekeeping.
5. Suggestions to correct those parts of the Operation that cause fatigue and discomfort.

It is recommended that workers receive a day's worth of instruction on CFM principles and methods so that their contributions can be better focused. Workers can also be very helpful in developing input to the Line Analysis program.

Supplier Relations

Building a defect free product is dependent upon receiving defect free material from suppliers. The non-value add cost of incoming inspection, test, and rework can be greatly reduced if suppliers adopt the Defect Prevention program. In addition, if suppliers operate under CFM, they are better able to economically deliver smaller lots of material in concert with our needs. Like all education processes, this process requires time, and patience rather than confrontation. The goal, of course, is to finally receive defect free product from suppliers so that the cost and delay due to inspection can be eliminated. This cost does not add value to the product and hence is waste. Suppliers are better able to impact such a program if they have a long term contract. This is consistent with the 'extended process concept' made famous by Dr. Deming, in which suppliers are part of the family. Such a long term relationship will reduce the importance of competitive bidding, and will result in lower cost.

Summary

In this chapter we provided examples showing how defects can be prevented from occurring. The need for cooperation between Engineering and Development has shown to be mandatory to prevent defects. Until *all* of these methods are operational, a company will suffer from defects which appear inevitable. Once educated in the skills of Defect Prevention, all employees look forward to defects as an exciting opportunity to exercise ingenuity in using these tools. A company that relies solely on inspection and test simply cannot compete with one which has implemented Defect Prevention.

---

[1]Grant, E. L. "Statistical Quality Control" New York: McGraw Hill, 1946, pp 34-36
[2]Montgomery, D. C. "Statistical Quality Control," New York: Wiley 1985
[3]Montgomery, D. C. "Design and Analysis of Experiments," 2nd Edition, New York: Wiley 1984

CHAPTER 8

Robotics, Automation and CIM

Introduction

Robotics and automation have caught the imagination of business publications and the popular press. Visions of the "Factory of the Future" usually involve an army of robots performing fabrication and complex assembly tasks, directed by computers with almost no human management intervention. Because of this vision, and the larger number of robots deployed in Japan than in the U.S., many view robots and automation as the principle path to competitiveness. While there are important applications for Robotics and automation, a fully implemented CFM system is a pre-requisite. Recall the example from Chapter 3, where high setup cost drove us to a Batch size of 447 units, even though our weekly need was only 20 units. Because a few units are needed for immediate production, a machine able to produce 447 units in a short time is required. Thus Batch production forces the purchase of capital equipment with 20 times the capability actually needed to meet customer demand. Once CFM is functioning, the demand for the product will fall to 20 per week, which is hardly a candidate for automation and robotics. Until all production processes have been functioning in Continuous Flow at the Takt time, you can not rationally determine the needed automation capacity. Further, the Manual Work Process at each operation must be perfected as a prerequisite for automation. Just as businessmen in the 1960's learned that computers can't help a poorly designed and functioning manual accounting method, the same is true of automation. Automation of imperfect manual methods may lead to failure, and the total loss of expensive equipment. In addition, automation may divert limited Manufacturing Engineering effort from CFM implementation, leading to a double fiasco. The greatest opportunity for waste elimination lies in prevention of defects, reduction of the Overhead costs associated with large inventories,

94

and reduction of waste labor. Robotics and Automation only reduce Direct Labor cost, which is not the biggest opportunity.

The authors have visited many factories in Japan, both CFM and Batch Production operations. The only robots seen were in fully functioning CFM factories. The Batch Production shops visited were machine tool and materials handling companies. No robotics or automation was in evidence. Therefore, it is safe to say: CFM first, automation second. With this caveat, however, there are several areas of the Factory of the Future vision well worth a practical effort.

In our discussion, we will include other technologies including CAD/CAM, Flexible Manufacturing systems, Group Technology, and Integrated Manufacturing.

Computer Aided Design and Manufacturing (CAD/CAM)

One of the greatest sources of waste affecting a company occurs in the development of a new product and its transfer to manufacture. The efficiency of the process can be measured by the character of effort during pilot production. Are Development and Manufacturing Engineers developing Mistake Proof Assembly Operations, Operations improvements and refining Process Controls? Or, are they busy with Engineering Change Orders and product redesign just to make it possible to manufacture. The latter is an utter waste, and prevents focus on productivity issues.

Far and away the greatest cause of this waste is the compartmentalization of Manufacturing Engineers from Development Engineers at the outset of design. We propose, in the Chapter on Strategy, a means of correcting that problem by Product Delivery Team concept. Assuming that this has first been affected, priority consideration should be given to a CAD/CAM system.

A computer-aided design and manufacturing system is a computer-based system to create and interact with a manufacturing data base, principally oriented towards increasing the design and Manufacturing engineer's productivity. Such systems have been commercially available for several years, and have found widespread applications in many industries. For example, computer-aided design has been used in electrical and electronics manufacturing (IBM, GE, Digital Equipment Corporation, Texas Instruments), petroleum and refinery machinery (EXXON, Shell), measurement and analytical instruments (Eastman, Kodak, Xerox), transportation (Ford, General Motors, Daimler-Benz) aerospace (Boeing, Lockheed, McDonnell-Douglas, Rockwell), chemical manufacturing (Allied Chemical, DuPont, Union Carbide), and heavy machinery manufacturing (Caterpillar Tractor, International Harvester).

These systems improve the design engineer's productivity in a number of areas. For example, in preparing engineering drawings, there are usually recurring features, or drawings that are frequently updated, the production and maintenance of these drawings with a CAD System is much more efficient than a manual system. Furthermore, bills of materials and technical illustrations are very quickly produced if they can be derived from data already stored in the system. Most CAD systems can perform calculations of area, volume, weight, deformation, thermal flux, and other characteristcs, or they can prepare input for larger general purpose computer programs. Design tasks that involve fitting a number of parts together are very efficiently done with many CAD systems.

Engineering estimators have developed CAD systems to associate, store, and recall graphical and text data for estimation purposes. Experience has shown that this approach is more productive than manual methods, and captures the cost information more effectively. In some companies, order entry can be integrated directly into the CAD systems. Major savings can occur in this area when an order must be tied to specific engineering drawings.

Finally, many CAM systems include software for producing the numerical control tapes and other output information used for either planning or performing the manufacturing process from information entered and stored in the system during design. This can greatly reduce the time and effort necessary to get a part into production. Despite this success, the link between computer-aided design and manufacturing is still rather tenuous. In fact, when engineers discuss CAD/CAM they are almost always referring to the design portion. Substantial work remains to tie design and manufacturing together into a truly computer integrated manufacturing system.

Computers play a central role in CAD/CAM systems. The optimum design of the computer system should be hierarchical in nature, as shown in Figure 8.1. The host computer system for the CAD work stations should also be connected to the CAM system, because many

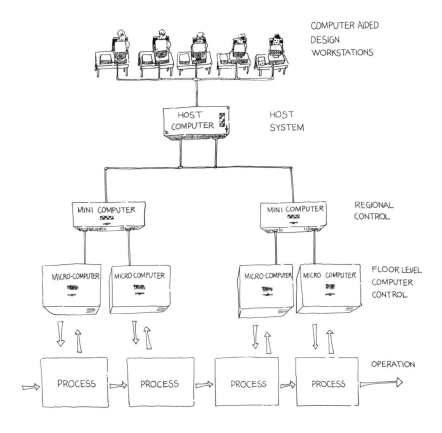

Fig. 8.1: Hierarchy of Computers in CAD/CAM

of the data bases should be shared. The fourth level of computer control for manufacturing should be microcomputer based, and will intereact with manufacturing equipment sensors for data capture. Minicomputers or super minicomputers may be required to supervise a given network of microcomputers on the factory floor. Very few companies have developed such a hierarchical computer system today. Software to operate such a system remains a significant barrier. Most of the hardware products to build this system are readily available.

All of these CAD/CAM tools can eliminate and prevent waste by improving the speed and accuracy of moving a design to manufacturing. A high level of training and competence is needed to make CAD/CAM attain this goal. The implementation should be taken one application at a time on a pay-as-you-go basis. Care must be taken to prevent an underproductive CAD system, equipped with expensive machines and computers, to become a source rather than an eliminator of waste. A vigilant focus on results must be maintained by management to prevent CAD/CAM from becoming an end unto itself.

Robots

For our purposes, a robot is defined as a machine with manipulators that can easily be programmed to do a variety of tasks automatically. A robot consists of the following components:

1. *One or more manipulators (arms)*
2. *A set of end effectors (hands)*
3. *A controller, and*
4. *Increasingly, sensors to provide information about the environment and feed back on performance of the work accomplished.*

The motivation for almost all current robot development is industrial application, to achieve the following goals:

1. *Increased productivity*
2. *Reduce costs*
3. *Overcome skilled labor shortages*
4. *Provide flexibility.*
5. *Improve Product Quality*
6. *Free human beings for boring and repetitive tasks or operations in hostile environments.*

Robots have been around a long time. The first industrial robot was a pick and place machine developed in the late 1950s. General Motors installed the first Unimation robot in 1962. As of 1983, there are approximately 43,000 robots in use in Japan, 9,400 robots in use in the United States, and 4,800 robots in use in West Germany. The typical cost of a robot is from $20,000 to $200,000, and it usually has a payback of between 2 and 4 years. The average cost breakdown of a robot system is 56 percent of total cost due to robot hardware, 28 percent of total costs for accessories and other peripheral equipment, and 16 percent of the total costs for installation.

From our discussion in the Chapter on the Importance of Quality, we saw examples of how advancing technology is shortening product lifetimes. This requires a compression of product development times. The time to develop and implement a robotic application is typically comparable to the product development time itself. Thus one must commit to robotic efforts very early, before the product is fully developed, or the sales volumes known. If the sales volumes do not materialize, a cost impact of disastrous proportions will result. Although in principle, a robot can be re-programmed for the next generation product, in practice this seldom occurs. Much of the reason is due to the fact that robot technology itself is quickly advancing, and that the robot asset of today is a liability in a few years. Thus the robot's total cost must generally be written off over an ever contracting product life. For products which have a long product life, robots can be effective.

Most of the current applications of robots involve metal working, materials handling, welding and painting. Some robots are used in assembly operations, although the United States is lagging far behind the Japanese in this area, principally because tolerance stack problems seriously impede automated assembly, and the United States is far behind Japan in improving overall process capability. Another impediment to Robotic assembly is caused by the increased demands of material delivery to the Robot. Material must be prepared in designed dispensers, precisely positioned, and loaded in the correct orientation. The cost and complexity of this task is often under-estimated. Robots with vision and tactile capability reduce the problems of tolerance stack and material delivery, but at a higher hardware and programming cost. We mentioned earlier that manual work methods must be perfected before Robotics can be implemented. It has often been found that, as a result of the effort to simplify the process for robotics, human workers can in fact achieve the cost goals for which robotics was justified.

The installation of robots usually leads to a reduction in the work force; in fact, the typical robot usually replaces between 1.6 and 4.0 workers. Robots generally lead to more efficient use of capital. For example, metal cutting equipment is typically used less than 27 percent of the time that it is actually available. A typical work piece in such a factory is usually worked on only 5 percent of the time. Robots can increase the output of a metal cutting operation between ten and fifty percent, and can decrease the amount of unused time by between thirty and three hundred percent. This improved utilization can only be realized if there is a steady *flow* of material to the robot, and the setup time and transport time are negligible. Thus the higher utilization is a result of the robot being part of a CFM environment. Statistics like this make the future look bright for robots. However, remember that they have their limits. Robots depend on processing sensor input. Human beings are much better for cognitive and interpretive tasks than robots. Furthermore, many tasks can not be easily pre-programmed, particularly in situations where decisions must be continually modified, and where decisions or actions cannot be reduced to simple equations.

As we have learned, the true production rate (Operation Time) for any piece of capital equipment must equal the Takt Time, i.e., the minutes per piece to meet customer schedule. This can only be determined after CFM is fully functioning.

Following CFM implementation, a priority of Robotic applications can be considered. Our driving goal is the elimination of waste. A few examples will illustrate the point. The Deere & Co. plant in Horicon, Wisconsin has an advanced and successful implementation of Continuous Flow Manufacturing. They have applied Robotics to replace MIG (Metal Inert Gas) welding with spot welding. Spot welding has many advantages, including less weld splatter (rework), less operation time per weld, and a much better appearance. The drawback of spot welding is that the positioning of the weld is critical to strength, and the electric current must be carefully controlled. With Robots, as with most automation, the uniformity of work is better than with manual methods. Thus, the Robot can more accurately repeat positioning, and can work faster than a human, with less risk. While many companies "set" the current level, it is subject to drift. Deere not only sets the level, they automatically measure the actual current going into the weld, and compare it to a reference. If the current goes out of spec, it will be corrected or shut down. This is another example of how the defect prevention philosophy should permeate the way we do business.

This Robotic application was justified because it removed an Operation Time pinch point that was shown to exist *after* CFM was fully implemented. It also eliminated a rework loop, eliminating waste and further improving productivity.

Robotics have also profitably been applied in painting, where the precision of distance from the nozzle to work can be more accurately controlled.

General Assembly type operations (except for PC insertion) need to be looked at critically for waste elimination, including overhead and programming costs. Some applications, such as picking parts from a jumbled bin are intellectually fascinating, but of questionable value. Find out how the parts got jumbled, and prevent its reoccurrence.

We are strongly in favor of all Robotic applications which are implemented to meet the Takt Time requirements of CFM. The number and range of such applications is rapidly increasing.

The United States does not have any formalized policy on the development of robotics and automation systems. The Japanese government, however, has an industrial policy on robotics. This policy is typical of the targeting that the Japanese government has done in other areas. The Japanese government coordinates and advances research on current robot manufacturing while accelerating industrial research and applications throughout the manufacturing sector. There are a number of major programs currently in place. These include:

1. *A seven year $150 million research program on the development of intelligent robots, sponsored and funded by the Ministry of International Trade and Industry (MITI). It will extend through early 1989.*
2. *Formation of the Japan Robot Leasing Company which, with funding via the Japan Development Bank, offers subsidized leasing arrangements to a wide range of potential customers.*
3. *Extra depreciation allowances on robots (an additional 12.5 percent per annum for 3 years) enabling firms to depreciate 52.5 percent of the purchase price the first year alone.*
4. *Direct, low interest loans through small business finance*

corporations to medium and small scale manufacturers purchasing robots.
5. *MITI support for development of a fully automated factory for small lot engineering components and assembly.*
6. *Twenty percent MITI funding of approximately 13 million dollars over the fiscal years 1977-1983 for development of a flexible manufacturing complex incorporating robots, automated manufacturing systems, and other advanced technology concepts.*

It is clear where the Japanese are going in this area, and that they plan to use robots and automation as a major competitive weapon in the future. Remember, Robots and Automation improve productivity, i.e., they reduce Direct Labor cost. The productive work force is not our greatest disadvantage. Rather, it is the Hidden Factory of Manufacturing Overhead which Robots cannot reduce. Therefore, implement all aspects of CFM before you tackle Robotics.

Flexible Manufacturing Systems

A flexible manufacturing system consists of one of several numerically controlled machines, an automated materials handling system between the machines, a computer control system over the materials and handling and the machine tools, and a group technology approach to manufacturing. Principal applications of these systems are in the production of families of parts, where the objective is to reduce lead time, reduce work in the process inventory, and to obtain better machine utilization.

Figure 8.2 shows the utilization of equipment that is typically achieved in batch machining. Notice that only 5 percent of the total time in the machine shop is generally spent on the tool, and of this time, only 30 percent represents actual machining time. The flexible manufacturing system (FMS) has been designed to combat some of these problems. Figure 8.3 shows the typical application characteristics of a flexible manufacturing system. Notice that the FMS can work extremely well in situations where the variety of parts produced are from medium to high and where the production volume is medium to high. In such situations, the output for employee per year with an FMS can be four times that of the traditional manufac-

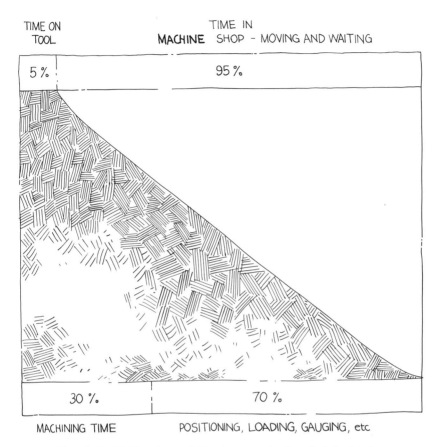

TIME ON TOOL | TIME IN MACHINE SHOP – MOVING AND WAITING

5 % | 95 %

30 % | 70 %

MACHINING TIME | POSITIONING, LOADING, GAUGING, etc

Fig. 8.2: Utilization of Equipment in Batch Machining

turing system, the stock turnover can be ten times per year greater, and the manufacturing lead time can be reduced by a factor of four.

While such performance statistics will not occur in every case, they are not unusual. Given these rather impressive statistics, it is not surprising that flexible manufacturing systems are being used in more and more factories today. However, the number of FMS installations in this country remains relatively small. Part of this may be the peculiarities of the capital expense justification procedure.

103

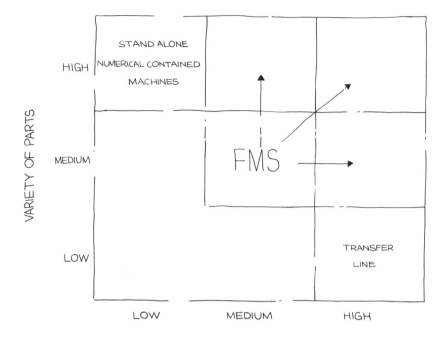

Fig. 8.3: Characteristics of a Typical
Flexible Manufacturing System

Traditionally, we have justified automation and robotics equipment on the basis of displacing labor dollars. With a flexible manufacturing system this will generally not lead to satisfactory savings. In fact, direct labor savings with an FMS will typically be fairly small. The real savings with an FMS come from reduced manufacturing cycle times, reduced WIP, improved product line flexibility, improved quality, and tying the FMS into an overall computer integrated manufacturing system. In other words, we are going to have to look at cost savings in the areas that we are traditionally not used to evaluating alternatives. It is probably best to regard the investment in a flexible manufacturing system as a strategic investment for the company, rather than a tactical one.

Improving Factory Productivity

Computers, robotics and automation, flexible manufacturing systems—all of these techniques can improve overall factory productivity. However, implementing these techniques properly in your business requires a carefully structured and properly executed plan. The key element in this plan is to start relatively small. The move toward the factory of the future should get there one day at a time. It is better to target specific areas for automation, and new technology strategies, and to bring these applications on one at a time.

In your overall effort to improve factory productivity, remember that improvement will come from the substitution of capital for labor. However, efforts to remove labor content by installing equipment—without developing the management system and procedures needed to realize the full potential of this equipment—will prove disastrous.

It is very important to keep the goal of automation in mind. If the goal is to displace direct labor cost, one must consider *all* the steps and costs needed to achieve this goal. One of the authors visited a Nissan plant and saw a human operator working behind nearly every Robot. Toyota's first efforts at automation did not displace workers. This failure was one of the reasons Toyota developed JIT. If labor displacement is the goal, then all portions of the job must be addressed. In addition to the work itself, one must include automatic loading, unloading, checking and correcting. Again, if labor cost reduction is your goal then the headcount of direct labor must be reduced, and indirect headcount should not increase. Otherwise you will end up with higher, not lower cost. Like all reform activities, one can well profit from Theodore Roosevelt's advice: *"Keep your head in the stars, but your feet on the ground."* CFM is a hard-headed plan to eliminate waste. Automation can and must play the same role. On balance, automation is more appropriate for capacity expansion and defect prevention than for labor displacement.

Computer Integrated Manufacturing (CIM)

Computer Integrated Manufacturing: CIM is replacing the more familiar term CAD/CAM. This new terminology emphasizes a total systems approach, recognizing inner relationships between design, manufacturing, production control, quality, materials, and other manufacturing functions. Consequently, CIM is a more general term than CAD/CAM, and can even be considered appropriate for manufacturing operations that have not been completely automated.

The principal emphasis on CIM is on the communication linkage between the various systems that drive the manufacturing process, as well as the support functions for direct manufacturing. These communication problems are non-trivial because of the way in which individual manufacturing and manufacturing support functions have been automated in the past. For example, design engineering has its own CAD software, manufacturing has CAM software to drive numerical control equipment, production planning and scheduling has its own inventory control software (such as MRP), and materials will have its own data base for inventory operations. However, the complete integration of these various sub-systems can result in significant savings, and can also provide a common data base which is of enormous potential value to the company.

It was the early successes with CAD and CAM that resulted in the first attempts in the 1980s to develop CIM. The intitial efforts were to standardize data bases between the various functions in manufacturing. The problem of integrating and standardizing data bases from various manufacturing functions is challenging. Even today, there are numerous examples of integrated data bases for production and inventory environments, yet very few of these have been successfully integrated with engineering systems to provide for automatic generation of bill of material data. Even fewer include the CAD/CAM geometry systems which allow automation of the down stream process planning and manufacturing functions. In other words, there is considerable work yet to do in the development of CIM.

Computer Integrated Manufacturing is a far reaching goal. Few plants have achieved it, and perhaps many companies never will. The CIM system represents the ultimate in manufacturing automation. However, one should not rush to hop on the CIM bandwagon too quickly. Before any automated system in a factory makes sense, you have to get the basic manufacturing operation running in control, and operating effectively. This means that the basic principles of continuous flow manufacturing are an initial first step in the development of any improved factory system.

Summary

The popular notion that the "Factory of the Future" technology is the path to Worldwide Business Competitiveness is not borne out by experience. A firm must have a fully functioning CFM flow prior to automation. CAD/CAM is recommended as the first automation tool worthy of consideration *following* CFM implementation. "Factory of the Future" tools must be justified on the Elimination of Waste principal, or not pursued.

The general recommendation in pursuing any of these methods is to start small. Apply a lot of intelligence and a little money. Make sure the method can pay its way, and that it does not become an end rather than a means to Waste elimination and Productivity improvement.

CHAPTER 9

DEVELOPING THE CORPORATE STRATEGY

The most important new factor in business is the necessity to become and remain cost competitive worldwide. It is no longer possible to rely on superior products or marketing alone. A corporation must be able to manufacture low cost defect free product. The transition from a Marketing or Technology driven corporate culture is not easy. Those companies which accept the challenge to become cost competitive on a worldwide basis will endure and prosper. Those which do not may ultimately fail.

The first step, then, is to make a commitment to become cost competitive worldwide. The next step is to develop objective measures of where you are versus competition, and where you need to be. The development of a schedule and implementation of a program to become competitive is the final step.

Objective Measures:

One of the key objectives of attaining the lowest cost of manufacture is the elimination of waste. The waste functions of a business are related to Defects (Scrap, Rework, Warranty) and to excessive Manufacturing Overhead. Waste is also generated by a poor interface between R&D and Manufacturing, or an ineffective Manufacturing Engineering effort.

It is very difficult to develop direct measures of costs of competitors, because the information is not public. There are, however, indirect objective measures which relate to competitive performance.

Inventory Turns Ratio:

A major thesis of this book is that, the higher the inventory turns, the lower the waste. Alternatively, the lower the inventory turns, the greater is the opportunity for profit improvement. At the production level, it is clear that a product with many defects is going to spend more time in rework, depressing inventory turns. Further, a slow moving inventory requires a large non-value add organization to move, count, transport, re-issue and manage the inventory. Low inventory turns is a measure of the cost of this effort.

Thus, in measuring the cost competitiveness of two organizations, inventory turns is decisive. As an example, Toyota is famous for nearly defect free, low cost production. Toyota turns inventory 70 times per year. Ford, although one of the best managed American companies, turns inventory 10.2 times per year. Reject rates on American auto parts are significantly higher than Toyota, Honda, etc. If Ford sets its sight on 70 turns per year, it must first eliminate waste to achieve that goal.

The calculation of Inventory Turns is based on information which is generally public. One divides the Cost of Goods Sold by the average Inventory, averaging from the beginning and end of the period. In calculating this figure, it is important to use quantities that relate to current operations. The Notes to the financial statement should be used to remove one-time, non-period charges. All competitors, particularly Japanese, should be included.

Once a competitive ranking has been developed, Management should set the goal to catch and surpass the leader. This will require the implementation of Continuous Flow Manufacturing *throughout* the corporation. It may also require a change in the relations between R&D and Manufacturing, to be discussed later. The Officers of the company must drive for higher inventory turns corporate wide, and not settle for the 'showcase' CFM or JIT examples prevalent in the U.S.

In addition to measuring the relative efficiency of manufacture, higher inventory turns is a competitive weapon. In good times it allows a company to make a higher profit. In bad times, it allows a company to earn an adequate return at lower prices.

Manufacturing Cycle Time

The Manufacturing Cycle Time is defined as the period between receiving an order and its ship date. It is also referred to as throughput time. It includes any custom engineering, as well as manufacturing and test. One of our CFM goals is to reduce Manufacturing Cycle Time below Customer Delivery Requirements. Assume customers in your industry are always willing to wait one week from order date to ship date. Then the Manufacturing Cycle Time should be less than five days. In this way, you can ship out of production rather than shipping from a finished goods inventory. This will avoid loading the factory production schedule with unsold product, reducing excess capital equipment capability, inventory, etc.

Manufacturing Cycle Time should also be regarded as a strategic weapon. Customers prefer to hold up order commitments as long as possible. This gives them more flexibility to meet their own changing demands and schedules. Thus, the vendor with the fastest lead time will be a preferred supplier.

Manufacturing Cycle Time includes the entire time from receiving an order to ship date. It includes Order Entry, any Custom Engineering as well as Manufacturing and Test. In many companies, Order Entry and Custom Engineering take as long as Manufacturing. The Custom Engineering can often be streamlined by building a 'Go' system based on variations from a baseline product. (See Chapter 3) A cooperative effort with Marketing and Manufacturing can sometimes reduce both the Engineering and Order Entry function to a check-off list ideally suited for a Personal Computer. The programming of the Personal Computer can include error checking, so that commonly occurring errors are prevented. Thus the PC becomes a White Collar Mistake Proof Operation, eliminating vexations and waste.

Product Cost

A factor of great importance is the estimated cost of competitors products versus your product. It is possible to make this determination without infringing on trade secrets or patents. The method is known as Benchmarking. It consists of purchasing a competitive product and estimating the cost of each component of material and labor on a functional basis. This will tell you where you are ahead, where behind, and provides a path for improvement.

You will be surprised at the cleverness of your competitor's engineers. Effectively you gain leverage on your R&D and Manufacturing Engineering dollars by giving your engineers the public domain knowledge of your competitors. Since your R&D expenditure is usually a small percent of that of the total industry, you increase your knowledge per dollar many fold. In performing Benchmarking, it is imperative to use only public information, and beware of patent infringements or confidential information.

A well documented case of benchmarking comes from the office photo copying industry.[1]

'It begins with product designers tearing apart existing machines to examine each and every part.' 'We take all 3000 parts in the copier,' said Takeomi Nagafuchi, Ricoh's Quality Control Manager, 'And we extensively test each and every one . . .' In benchmarking competitive products, Canon found that, by replacing their dry toner with the competitor's wet toner, they cut power consumption in half. Minolta found they could replace 27 microswitches with a single part.

Xerox could not believe that their manufacturing cost was the same as Canon's selling price. Xerox engineers went through phases of anger, incredulity, and denial, and then they went to work. They succeeded in developing a superior product at competitive cost, the 10 Series Copier. Xerox has *increased* market share at the expense of the Japanese each year for the last three years.

Benchmarking can be carried further by determining manufacturing process. How does the cost of fabrication of functional equivalents compare with your cost? What types of material are used? How well does their machine perform? Xerox performed this and found that they had used many custom, expensive parts that could be replaced by functional equivalents at much lower cost.

The Ford Motor Company astounded the industry with strong profitability in 1986, selling approximately 500,000 of the new Taurus. 'Ford engineers tore apart competitiors' cars and adopted many of their best features for the Taurus.'[2]

Ability To Compete Internationally

Firms that presently or potentially face foreign competition must develop a plan to become cost competitive worldwide. To put this plan in practice, many firms have set the following goals:

Step 1: Be able to build the product in U.S. and compete with Japanese imports.

Step 2: *Be able to build the product in Japan and compete in*
the Japanese domestic market.
Step 3: *Be able to build the product in the U.S. and compete*
in the Japanese domestic market.

How do firms implement the program?

A Window On The East?

One advantage that Xerox enjoyed in their effort was the input of
their Japanese affiliate, Fuji-Xerox. Deere and Co. is one of the
U.S. leaders in CFM implementation at their Horicon, Wisconsin
works. Where did they hear about CFM? From their Japanese
affiliate, Yanmar. The Horicon works builds riding lawn mowers,
front cutting mowers, lawn tractors, etc. Determined management
stated in 1983 that 'There will be no more price increases!' Horicon
implemented CFM, and developed a new Compact Utility Tractor to
meet Kuboto head on. Deere has increasingly taken market share
away from the Japanese.

A surprising number of American firms operate in Japan. The list
includes IBM, Texas Instruments, Pfizer, 3M, Hewlett-Packard, and
many other famous names. The return on investment of American
firms in Japan averages 19%, twice as great as U.S. return on investment in France and Britain.[3]

Successful participation in Japan exposes a company to the rigors
of the world's most competitive market, and is an invaluable source
of information. The popular wisdom that Japan is a closed economy
must be challenged in light of the fact that over 1500 'foreign-
capital' companies operate in Japan, including two-thirds of the top
U.S. industrial firms. Entry into Japan should be viewed as a major
strategic commitment, with intelligence as important a return as
profit. The commitment must begin with the American Team learning the Japanese language and distribution system. Their government is now less insistent on Japanese partnership. The ideal effort is
one in which you 'go it alone.' This requires more effort, but
protects proprietary technology.

Popular wisdom also holds that the Japanese can only copy
technology, then perfect the manufacturing method. In fact, it was
the Japanese who were first in marrying electronics to cameras, a

transition the Germans failed to make. They are leaders in robotics, ceramic engine components, turbo chargers, etc. At present there are, in Japan, more than 200 firms working in the field of new ceramic materials, and 157 working in biotechnology. Since 1965, Japan's investment in R&D has more than tripled, while the U.S. has only grown 32%.[4] Japan is the most fiercely competitive market in the world. Your Japanese subsidiary must compete in this arena, and will be toughened by the experience. Companies that work hard, try to meet Japanese demands for quality, cost, performance, and don't give up, have done well. We already know that a Batch Production operation can't achieve these goals and is doomed. But a CFM operation can compete, and will be an invaluable source of information which may be vital to your company's well being.

Despite the success of many U.S. firms in Japan, the allegation that the Japanese market is closed persists. In fact, the Japanese once did protect their industries. These tariff barriers have largely been dismantled since 1970.[5] Now the complaint is that 'non-tariff' barriers are the obstacle. In the book, 'Can America Compete?', Robert Lawrence argues that:

The loudest complaints about the closed nature of the Japanese market often come from U.S. companies that have great trouble competing with Japan in the United States and hence are unlikely to benefit from . . . the Japanese market.

Entry into the Japanese market is not without risk. Procter & Gamble experienced difficulty with distribution, advertising and product. P&G has remedied these problems, and is expected to improve operations in 1987.[6]

Whether or not your company establishes a business in Japan, you must remain abreast of their developments, particularly in new products as discussed in competitive benchmarking.

Growth Rate

Growth rate can be a vital measure of manufacturing strength. If a competitor is growing at a markedly higher rate, a serious threat exists. We shall later give examples where this phenomena proved fatal to the slow growing company.

High growth is primarily generated by exciting new products, by lower prices or entry into new markets. All of these factors are in fact driven by manufacturing efficiency. New products are most effective if they can be rapidly developed and put into production at low cost with no defects. This performance *requires* a strong bridge between Manufacturing and R&D. Low Price is again the result of Manufacturing efficiency and hence high inventory turns. The ability to sell in a new market is also related to these two factors.

The corporation should establish a strategic goal of growing as fast or faster than any worldwide competitor. It must determine the cause of higher growth on the part of a competitor and develop a strategy to overcome the disadvantage, be it low cost, a new product or market. This effort is the primary responsibility of Marketing. R&D must remain alert to growth opportunities related to new technology.

Growth Rate and Low Price

In addition to new products and technologies, low price is a powerful stimulant to demand. We have seen how Henry Ford reduced price by 60%, increased sales from $4 million to $206 million, and increased the profit percentage from 22 to 27%. We have seen the same phenomenon in VCR pricing in the last few years.

In determining if a price cut is advisable, Marketing must estimate what additional sales volume could be developed. This strategy might be used to open a foreign (why not Japan!) market. With the data from marketing, one uses Line Analysis with higher Daily Going Rates to determine which Operations have Pinch points (Chapter 4). If only a few are found, and can be eliminated with minor investment, a new higher plant capacity has been found. A key advantage of CFM is that production rates can be ramped up with little increase in WIP. Thus plant space requirements grow more slowly versus production increases than in Batch Production. The marginal gross profit will flow to the bottom line. This strategy is particularly important in a growing market. A recent example will illustrate the danger of not being prepared, or not responding to rapid growth.

Consider the example of Tohatsu. Ever heard of them? You'll soon learn why you haven't. In the early 1950's Tohatsu was the leader in the Japanese motorcycle market. With a 24% market share, 8% profit on sales and little debt, its strength was unchallenged. Honda had less than 20% of the market, and was debt ridden. Honda developed a high inventory turns capability based on JIT. They then cut prices, and increased sales. Although the margins were low, the high inventory turns yielded an adequate return on investment. This is an example of the Supermarket analogy. Honda cut prices to stimulate volume while Tohatsu played it safe at high prices. Within a decade, Honda had 65% of the market and earned 10% profit on sales. Tohatsu had 4% of the market and was bankrupt.

In the first Quarter of 1987, sales of personal computers soared by over 30%. Much of the credit for the increased sales is given to lower prices. (Wall Street Journal, 4/24/87)

In Batch production, the Inventory Turns is not easily increased. Thus sales volume can only be increased by more capital equipment, more plant and more people. And worst of all, more Work in Process inventory. In addition to the built-in cost disadvantage, Batch production suffers from a long cycle time to react to market growth or decline. Production rates are ramped up by increasing Batch sizes, further lengthening cycle time and reducing responsiveness to market changes.

Opportunities for rapid growth via low prices should be actively sought out and carefully evaluated with the eye toward implementation.

Rapid Development and Cost Reduction

One of our strategic goals is to be able to move a new product from the concept stage to low cost, defect free production at least as fast as our best competitor. How can we achieve this goal?

Recall the discussion on Design for Manufacture in the chapter on Defect Prevention. We spoke of the need for early involvement of manufacturing engineers in design of new products. Most of us who have put new products into production are all too familiar with the Engineering Change Order (ECO). When a new product is designed solely by R&D, the most common goal is to meet marketing's functional requirement. When the pilot production (or worse, full production) begins, manufacturing will find tolerance errors, difficult or impossible assembly tasks, new and unstable processes,

115

new vendors, new components and limited test procedures. Then the ECO start flying in earnest to try to correct these problems. Little or no effort is available to do 'optional' work like developing Mistake Proof Operations, Design for Manufacture, Designed Experiments, etc. In some companies, the non-productive ECO process costs 20% of the R&D cost. The solution is obvious: New products must be developed by a Product Delivery Team which includes Manufacturing Engineers and Technicians as well as Development Engineers. Xerox used this concept in the development of 10 Series Copiers. They brought a product with more features, and lower cost more swiftly into trouble free production than any prior product. Xerox reversed years of steadily declining market share and started gaining market share.

How do the Japanese develop a strong bridge between Manufacturing and R&D? Ninety percent of all newly graduated Japanese engineers spend their first two years of employ working on the shop floor. Their Manufacturing Engineers are of equal intellectual caliber to their R&D counterparts. Another major difference that helps bring down barriers and allow smoother progress is the Japanese policy of Job Rotation across functions.

Benefit of the Product Delivery Team

One of the key benefits of the Product Delivery Team concept is that the design of the product will be consistent with the manufacturing technology which is already in, or can be brought into, the plant. Assume you have a factory with specialized automated equipment manufacturing the present product. If the new product can't be run on existing equipment, you have thrown away a factory! This is, regrettably, not a hypothetical example. By making manufacturing constraints a part of the development process, the related ECO and Plant Obsolescence can be prevented.

The manufacturing personnel can bring the manufacturing processes under control in the development stage using Statistical Process Control and Designed Experiments. Manufacturing can also provide insight into the Design for Manufacture criteria to prevent assembly problems.

As processes leave the lab and are tried in production, problems often arise. The Product Delivery Team will work the Line Personnel in applying Designed Experiments to continually reduce defects and improve yield. The Product Delivery Team will follow the product into the customers hands, assuring satisfaction.

We must put intelligence back to work in the factory? How? The product Delivery Team is the ideal entry point for many new Engineering and MBA graduates. In this way they will be exposed to all the crucial disciplines of business: Product Definition, Development, implementation into CFM production, and Market Acceptance. Their intelligence, energy and enthusiasm will, if properly managed, allow your company to become the competitive leader. In addition, the experience will build a better class for future managers.

There has been criticism that the training of U.S. executives does not adequately prepare them for cost effective manufacturing. A recent report of the National Academy of Engineering concurs with this evaluation:

Preparation of U.S. executives allow them to remain aloof from the factory floor and the people expert in the day-to-day task of making products. If Americans entering leading business schools are technologically "illiterate," the current business school curriculum is likely to distance them farther from engineering and technology and perhaps even increase their disdain for hands-on experience. Once an MBA joins a typical company, opportunities for experience on the factory floor are limited and sometimes discouraged, with the result that many people managing U.S. companies are unfamiliar with crucial parts of the firm's operations. It is thus no surprise that U.S. corporations tend to be drawn to legal or financial solutions rather than technical ones.

This report neglects the fact that top U.S. executives are highly adaptable. No matter what their background, if manufacturing is required for success, they will learn manufacturing! Indeed, this book was written to assist this process. Nevertheless, the Product Delivery Team is a better entry point for young MBA than the Executive Suite.

As you will read in the chapter on IBM, indirect personnel who were temporarily assigned to CFM implementation loved it so much that they wanted to stay in Manufacturing.

These are exciting, interesting, and fulfilling efforts which generate a great feeling of accomplishment and self worth. In addition to eliminating financial waste, CFM is probably the key to avoiding Human and Management Waste.

You may be developing a new product, or re-designing an old one to incorporate needed change. In either case, consider the creation of a dedicated Product Delivery Team. The Team will have focus, ownership, esprit-de-corps, and avoids the paralyzing 'we-they' polarization of Design versus Manufacturing Engineers. With this focus, the team will be on the shop floor solving problems.

Market Share

Competitive cost position is often determined by manufacturing experience. This is particularly true in the Process industries, where yield largely determines cost. You will recall that, in the semiconductor industry, the Japanese were first to market the 64K RAM chip in 1981. By 1983, when major American competitors entered the fray, the Japanese yields, hence cost was far better. Despite furious assaults, the Japanese held on to 50% market share.

A commanding market share conveys the advantage of more manufacturing experience, and more opportunity to improve. By failing to stay at parity in terms of market share, the opportunity to achieve cost parity is also jeopardized.

Thus in the early growth phases of a new market, market share is more important than immediate profit. If market share is not maintained, the whole investment related to that product is jeopardized.

Return on Investment (ROI)

Return on Investment, although a valid measure of manufacturing efficiency, is not as precise as inventory turns.

In an industry where inventory is difficult to measure (Oil, Mining, Forest Products, etc.), ROI is an important criteria in ranking competitors. Again, management must set its goal of catching and surpassing its best competitor worldwide, assuming that it is efficient in its use of capital.

Return on Sales

Return on Sales gives little insight into relative manufacturing efficiency. It is more related to the condition of the market, rising with high demand, and vice versa.

One of the leading exponents of manufacturing cost dominance was Andrew Carnegie. He refused to rate managers on profit, but rather on their ability to drive down cost. This led Carnegie Steel (later U.S. Steel) to develop the 'hard driving' furnace method, yielding over 12 'heats' per day rather than the industry standard of 4. In downturns, Carnegie made money when all others lost, because his costs were lower. He rightly regarded profit as a management measure less important than cost.

Although Return on Sales is interesting, it is less valuable for our analysis.

Accounting Systems

In Chapter 4, we discussed the problems faced by industries involved in seasonal production. One of their motivations for producing finished goods inventory was the penalty imposed by a fixed high Manufacturing Overhead upon a low production volume. Manufacturing Overhead is a catch-all cover for many functions which, in CFM, will be regarded as waste. This large cost can be hidden in inventory during slack periods, and *hopefully* can be re-couped when the product is subsequently sold. Manufacturing Overhead is usually allocated as a percentage of Direct Labor cost, and is typically 3-5 times as great. A given Department can therefore "look good" if it can reduce Direct Labor cost, as it avoids the much larger allocation of Manufacturing Overhead. This increases the impetus to buy expensive machines with tremendous production rates, and to build large batches of material. In this way, the allocated cost of Manufacturing Overhead burden is shifted to other departments. In the name of labor efficiency, excess capital equipment and inventory is used, further increasing Manufacturing Overhead. To solve a problem, it is first necessary to expose it. It is strongly recommended that Manufacturing Overhead be treated as a monthly period cost, in the same way Selling and General Administrative costs are reported. If

Accounting cannot accept this change, then it should at least be used for internal measurements of manufacturing management. Manufacturing Overhead should not be apportioned based on direct labor cost, but on the overhead costs actually used by each department. For example, assume a department reduces lot sizes and WIP to the point that it doesn't use the stockroom. It should no longer pay the cost and space of the stockroom and its personnel. Other jobs must be found for them. If a department totally eliminates defects, it should only pay for the minor QC surveillance cost. A department should only pay depreciation on machines it owns. Managers will then work toward real waste elimination to cut their overhead allocation. This solves real problems, rather than manipulating direct labor cost to reduce the overhead charge.

The details and functions of Manufacturing Overhead must be clearly displayed, and a schedule set to reach a target reduction. This goal setting will prioritize CFM efforts to eliminate waste. Accounting should display this detail versus last month, quarter and year.

Accounting should adopt the Seven Measures of Manufacturing efficiency discussed below in the monthly accounting report, showing trends versus last month, quarter and year and versus competitors. In addition, Accounting should create a reporting method with manufacturing to capture the cost of scrap, rework, inspection, and test.

Like all other aspects of the business, Accounting must examine its own functions with management to determine if they add value. In particular, the value of the effort of capturing detailed direct labor cost is less important when it no longer relieves Overhead.

Review

The key manufacturing parameters which rank competitors are, in order of importance:

SEVEN STRATEGIC MEASURES OF MANUFACTURING STRENGTH

Parameter	Best Competitor	Your Position	Schedule Date to Surpass Competitor
1. Inventory Turns Ratio			
2. Manufacturing Cycle Time			
3. Product Cost			
4. Ability to Compete (Internationally)			
5. Growth Rate			
6. Market Share			
7. Return on Investment			

It should not be inferred that these are the only important financial measures, but they are the engines which drive manufacturing competitiveness. Top management must define their present position, set a schedule date to surpass all competitors, and continually monitor progress.

Education

In the introduction, we pointed out that one of the Japanese secrets was that their top management attended lectures on quality. It is essential that top management become involved to the extent that they drive the organization to attain the goals of the Seven Strategic Measures.

Clearly the methods described in this book are not typical of the prevailing Batch production methods. To make the transition to low cost, defect free manufacture requires teamwork. This is only possible if there are shared goals among management, marketing, engineering and manufacturing. Shared goals are only possible through broad based education. This can be accomplished through inhouse developed courses or training by outside sources. In either case, the educational process should precede all other efforts. Personnel should be exposed to all the CFM tools in sufficient depth for implementation. This should include all the tools, including Line Analysis, The Pull System, Rapid Setup, Operation Improvement, Mistake Proof Operations, etc.

Implementation

Following education, it is important to pick a target process which can show significant progress. This will demonstrate the power of the system, and give CFM implementation a good start. Ideally, it is best to start by implementing the Pull System at Final Assembly and working backward. Alternatively, you may wish to begin with a Process which has a very high defect rate. In any case, the following guides should be followed in selecting the target. The ideal process should have:

1. *A Determined Manager*
2. *Processing in Large Batches*
3. *Significant Defects and Long Setup Times*
4. *Pinch Points which are restricting output (known and unknown)*
5. *A process which is stabilized (few ECO)*

The first step is to perform Line Analysis. This will provide the priority and determination of the proper CFM tools, such as Rapid Setup, Defect Prevention, etc.

The target process should be of such a size that those educated in CFM are able to overwhelm early problems. Following this success, education can be extended, and the process expanded.

It is ideal to have top executives involved or aware of the program. If this is not possible initially, the first success should be brought to their attention. The effort should be continually expanded to improve corporate wide profitability, not just a showcase. A target date must be established by which time all plants are running under CFM. Otherwise, it is too easy to maintain the status quo of high cost and high defect rates. In the past, this has not been Manufacturing's problem. Manufacturing was measured primarily on ability to ship. With the elevation in strategic authority of Manufacturing comes the corresponding increase in strategic responsibility to make the company cost competitive.

Continual Improvement

In the discussion of Continuous Flow Manufacturing, we stated that it is a journey, not a destination. There will never be a time when costs are finally and forever at their lowest cost. There will always be new products, new processes and change which will introduce new defects. New technology will make this process permanent.

At the corporate level, a company's ranking versus the Seven Strategic Measures will always be challenged by new competition, changes in the market, etc. Thus the philosophy of continual Improvement of CFM must be carried to the Boardroom.

In his masterful study of the rise and fall of major civilizations, Arnold Toynbee has noted an interesting phenomenon:

A society that is in adversity, and is challenged just below the breaking point, will grow to a higher plane of strength and civilization. The civilization will continue to grow if each challenge, successfully met, leads to a new challenge. A society which is not challenged, but which is rich and complacent, inevitably declines and is destroyed.

The same phenomenon no doubt operates in corporate life. It is therefore not only desirable, it is management's responsibility, to vigorously face challenges, rather than avoid opportunities or surrender positions which have become uncomfortable.

What is the result of this process of continual challenge and improvement?

- *Better Quality, Lower Priced Products for the Consumer*
- *Higher Sales, Higher Profits and a Better Return on Investment for the Shareholder*
- *Stable and More Interesting Employment for the Worker*
- *Greater Personal Satisfaction and Rewards for the Professional and Management Staffs*

Summary

In this chapter, we developed the important measures of cost competitiveness. A company must set goals based on these measures as the driving force for all improvement efforts. For Manufacturing to attain the goal of lowest cost, defect free product, teamwork with Marketing and R&D is essential. Examples of this teamwork included the effort on Benchmarking competitor's cost and the Product Delivery Team.

---

[1]Jacobsen, G. & Hillkirk, J., 'Xerox, American Samurai,' New York: Macmillan, 1986, p. 107

[2]Newsweek, Nov. 24, 1986

[3]Abegglen, J. & Stalk, G., 'Kaisha', pg. 215

[4]Abegglen, on cit.

[5]Christopher, R. G., 'Second to None: American Companies in Japan', New York: Crown, 1986

[6]Forbes, Dec. 15, 1986

[7]White, R. R., "Education for the Manufacturing World of the Future," Washington, D.C.: National Academy Press, 1985, pg 29.

[8]Porter, M. "Competitive Strategy," New York: Free Press, 1980.

CHAPTER 10

CONTINUOUS FLOW MANUFACTURING AT IBM

Introduction

Continuous Flow Maunfacturing has been applied at IBM as part of the company's efforts to become the lowest cost producer. Many people mistakenly believe that JIT is simply an inventory reduction plan, rather than an integrated manufacturing system including Rapid Setup, Process Flow Operations Improvement, Defect Prevention, etc. For this reason, IBM renamed JIT, and called it Continuous Flow Manufacturing (CFM). CFM includes all the JIT tools and support described thus far, but is guided by Line Analysis. One of IBM's definitions of CFM is a process which:

- *Yields an optimally balanced manufacturing line with no waste.*
- *Uses the "Pull System."*
- *Results in lowest cost product with no defects and is delivered on time.*

Continuous Flow Manufacturing is a strategy involving *all functions*, including Marketing, Development, and Manufacturing in a cooperative, not confrontational effort, to achieve goals common to all. The program is dedicated to simplicity and continuous ongoing improvement in reducing costs, improving quality and increasing market responsiveness. Much of CFM is not new, most of the ideas come from Henry Ford. CFM is not complicated; most of it is common sense management. To implement the CFM philosophy into the Manufacturing process requires that everyone work toward the same objective. The figure below (fig. 10.1) shows all the functions which support CFM implementation circling manufacturing. Notice that manufacturing has a dual role. Manufacturing has the role of being the leader of the implementation of CFM, as well as being a member of the implementation team. The other functions

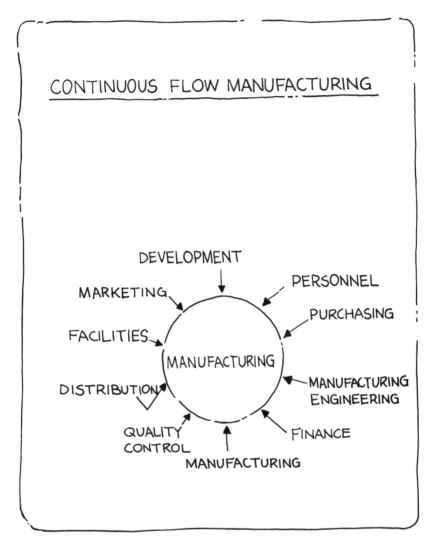

Fig. 10.1: CFM Implementation Support

must provide manufacturing all the necessary support and contribute to the corporate strategy.

One of the most important facts about CFM is that it WILL WORK IN ANY MANUFACTURING APPLICATION: THERE ARE *NO* EXCEPTIONS. As CFM was being introduced in IBM people were constantly saying that CFM was good, but, they had a unique situation and it won't work on our process. To prove conclusively that CFM concepts worked in different manufacturing environments IBM established pilot work in three diverse manufacturing processes. They were:

- *A process line at a semiconductor plant*
- *A system assembly line*
- *A PC card assembly line*

IBM already had experience with JIT implementation, some successful and some not. The experience on the Super Pilot Lines showed why the failures occurred, and how the following Line Analysis procedures would have allowed success to be achieved with all the experiences prior to the Super Pilot Lines.

As an example of the success of the project, in the Semiconductor Plant, on the average, Cycle Time was cut by 79%, Work in Process was reduced by 64% and Productivity was increased 30%. Another key factor was that morale was significantly improved. Morale improved dramatically in all cases where team participation has been emphasized, cross training implemented, work scopes expanded and measuring people on number of pieces produced, was eliminated. All three Super Pilot Lines showed remarkable improvement, as shown by the summary data at the end of this chapter.

With the implementation of CFM using Line Analysis, IBM has focused on three fundamental principles:

- *Total People Involvement*
- *Total Quality Control*
- *Elimination of Waste*

IBM has alway believed that people are their most valued asset. Because of this IBM has emphasized suggestion programs and quality circles to elicit ideas. CFM provides a disciplined team work environment that brings sharper focus and quicker reaction to good ideas and is totally compatible with the IBM suggestion program. With CFM there is more emphasis on capitalizing on the expertise of the person doing a particular job. After all who knows more about a particular job than the person that has been performing it for a long time. People whose livelihood depends on how well they perform the operation are often best qualified. Unfortunately, how well they have performed is often evaluated based on how many pieces have been produced in a given period of time. Management has spent years conditioning people to respond to production numbers. People were told if they wanted a job with more responsibility and a higher earning potential, they must produce more. This had motivated people to whatever extremes were necessary to get more productivity. However, because of the narrowness of their work scope and the constant focus on quantity produced, people didn't have time to contribute beyond their assigned responsibility. The number of parts produced has been de-emphasized, and instead the emphasis is on defect free parts and the production of only what is needed when it is needed. The goal is to meet the daily going rate demand, team work, and broadening the scope of responsibility. The efficiencies have improved tremendously when people have been given the opportunity to get involved with designing and implementing improvements. As a result of the CFM philosophy, phenomenal savings have occurred.

In one IBM plant, the materials manager returned from a series of work shops on JIT and decided to implement JIT into a line which had fairly stable schedules and a limited number of special features on the product. It was due to these attributes that he decided this would be the ideal pilot. During the implementation he encountered many problems and frustrations in implementing JIT. The major frustration was due to the fact that the team started to implement some of the JIT tools without previously doing Line Analysis. Through trial and error, they were finally able to overcome these frustrations. Eventually their perseverance started to pay off. Without doing the Line Analysis first, a great deal of time was wasted with trial and error implementation techniques. More analytical work through Line Analysis would have allowed the implementation team to identify what was needed for good results much faster. However, a year and a half later, productivity had increased by 130 percent and their quality improved to the point that quality control people checked on a sample basis only. The product yield had improved by 52 percent. The departments had been working excessive overtime and today they are, with few exceptions, working forty hour weeks. Often they finish their weekly schedules early on Friday afternoons. This creates available time for employee and technical support groups to hold work sessions that continually improves the processes. The people also receive more training on the CFM principles and concepts. All of these results were a product of all the people working together redesigning the layout of the line. Each employee on the line learned how to perform all the operations. They initiated the idea for a portable work station. One of the people suggested they test two machines at a time instead of one. This has also resulted in no missed shipments in over a year, and their daily rate of assembly of machines has increased by a factor of three. However, to the people, the largest benefit has been the improvement of morale and teamwork.

Total Quality Control (Also Called Defect Prevention)

When we get the people involved with Total Quality Control, they must be conditioned with the idea that it is an absolute. There must be quality at the source with all personnel responsible for their own quality, with the ultimate objective of each operation using mistake proof assembly methods, successive checks, etc. Traditional quality control reliance on inspection only must be eliminated. Quality cannot be inspected into the product. Defects must be prevented from happening, or found at the source and corrected before moving to the next operation.

Elimination of Waste

Any element of a process (not just a manufacturing process) that does not contribute to value added should be considered waste. Once identified, these non-value added elements should be eliminated or made more efficient with the ultimate objective of eliminating them. These three basic principles are the keys to the success that can be achieved with the implementation of the CFM philosophy. To make dramatic improvements in our production system the following CFM tools received focus:

- *Line Analysis*
- *Pull System Utilization*
- *Set Up Reduction*
- *Defect Prevention*
- *Process Flow Improvement*
- *Operation Improvement*

Total success can only be achieved by doing a Line Analysis first, which includes doing a detailed Flow Diagram of the process that has been selected as the CFM pilot line. Only by Line Analysis can the full scope of problems and opportunities be recognized. Failure to do Line Analysis is responsible for most CFM failures.

Line Analysis

A Line Analysis is needed to determine the leverage points which, if improved, will result in increased Manufacturing efficiency. It also allows you to implement the "Pull" system, and the lot size to be reduced. Line Analysis can be done manually or with simulation programs which are available in the software market. A simulation program should be selected that would, at least, work with the following inputs: 1) the operations contained in the process, 2) process time, 3) capacity, 4) daily going rate, 5) setup times and/or frequency, 6) rework loops, 7) transportation time and/or size of transport lot size, and 8) shifts to be worked. The model should track utilization of capacity and the number of units left waiting at each operation at the end of each day. The model should provide output that includes: 1) a copy of input data tables, 2) percent utilization (kanban design criteria), 3) capacity (this will also identify pinch points, excess capacity for growth, and kanban design criteria), 4) inventory queues in front of each operation, 5) total wip in the line (measure of line condition), 6) cycle times (line capacity and line status), 7) maximum capability of the line and 8) takt time of the operations and processes. The model should determine the hands on cycle time by finding the average number of days required for an average lot to go through the manufacturing line. As a precaution, at the end of the run the model should validate that steady state conditions prevail, by comparing the output plus fallout with the input. A discrepancy is an indication that the queues have not stabilized and an appropriate message appears on the screen and printer output. The simulation program should, at least, be able to solve for wip and cycle time using the capacity specified by the user, which is used to understand current pinch points and understand utilization required for the design of kanbans. The program should be used in a "what-if" mode, and as you input lot sizes, you will ulitmately encounter an operation that has a "Pinch Point." It may be a setup time that is too long or too slow an operation time, etc. This is the first priority of Manufacturing Engineering. Continued reduction of the lot size exposes more "pinch points". Thus, a prioritized list of efforts can be developed, and the limitations of the Process can be better understood if the right simulation program is selected.

One of the first locations to use a simulation program found it so easy and basic that they did a manual simulation to verify the results they got from using the program. They did this by taking a floor plan of the manufacturing floor and tracing the flow of the product with string, with paper symbols for the operations. The results of this exercise proved that the simulation program was correct and they could continue the implementation process.

However, to get started, it is absolutely necessary for the implementation team to have a thorough understanding of the selected pilot line. One of our first attempts at doing a line simulation proved this requirement to be true. The managers and people that supported one of the CFM pilot lines met in a conference room to do a line flow and line analysis. Once they had gathered all the required information it was fed into the simulation program and to their amazement the output showed the present actual cycle time was better than the cycle time predicted by the model. The implementation team very carefully went through their flow diagram to make sure they had not added any unnecessary steps and that the numbers they had used were correct. They re-input the data and the results were the same as before. This came as quite a shock, generally the model will show the current line to be very inefficient. Someone in the group suggested that the Manufacturing technician, responsible for this line, be called in to make sure they had not left anything out of their process information. The technician spent some time analyzing their data and concluded the line they were dealing with was slightly different than had been diagrammed. It is important to have some of the people that work with the subject line on a regular basis involved when doing the Line Analysis. When the CFM philosophy is being taught there are generally representatives from several different support disciplines in attendance. One of the most surprising things found is that the people that support the manufacturing lines often do not have sufficient knowledge of the line which is necessary to give meaningful support. This is generally due to them not having ongoing contact to stay current with line activity plus focus is often narrow, therefore, no one has complete view of the line. This is not good enough for Line Analysis and further supports the need to bring in line technician and key operators. Once the Line Flow Chart has been brought up to date and the data retrieved to fit the new flow, the simulation program was rerun. The output from this new run showed where the "pinch" points would occur as lot sizes were reduced. It identified which Operation in the Process was the pinch point, and whether it was caused by Setup Time, Operation Time, Defects, etc.

Pull System

Before attacking the problems within operations identified in Line analysis, the Pull System needs to be implemented. A Pull System is a discipline that pulls the product through the process in defined lot sizes. The Pull System starts at the end of the line and pulls product off the line as the customer demands it, no more or no less. The customer may be the next operation, the next Process or the Customer for the finished product. The customer demand sets the pace from the end of the line back through the process to the beginning of the line. The Line Simulation program will usually show that, even with present problems, you can safely reduce the lot size far below the level at which you have been running under Batch Production without encountering a "Pinch" point. In one case, 75% of the inventory was taken off the line, and the operators didn't even miss it. Thus there were immediate benefits from moving right into the "Pull" system after Line Simulation.

Traditionally the Push System has been used, which says we push product through the processes, building as much product at each operation as could be built in a designated time. The Push System requires large quantities of work in process and warehouses full of inventory. The Pull system requires defect free parts to be delivered when needed, in quantities needed to support the daily going rate. From this simulation output one of the things learned will be the optimum lot size (number of units processed at one time for a given operation) for the line the way it is currently described. Transportation time will also be recognized as a "Pinch" point, and the line must be re-laid out for a continuous flow of the product, or a Temporary-Kanban must be implemented as described later. As smaller and smaller lot sizes are simulated, more and more "Pinch" points will be discovered, which are problems that must be solved. Until the primary "Pinch" point is transportation time between Operations, the line does not have to be physically re-laid out for a continuous flow of the product. When this does occur it may not be physically possible to move machines, due to cost or other constraints.

To overcome this and other problems, and to approach the benefits of CFM, temporary kanbans were developed and implemented. The temporary kanbans were used when a regular Kanban would not maintain production demand. A regular kanban is determined by Line Analysis and requires no special attention. It only requires a physical container that holds or contains the designated kanban quantity. It may be a square painted on the floor which indicates the number of units in the kanban or a container which will hold the kanban quantity. Kanbans are positioned at the input and output of each operation, and hence at the beginning and end of the process. The input and output of normal kanbans can be visually seen from the operations they support (see fig. 10.2).

The temporary kanbans were put in place to compensate for: long set-up times, machine down time, machines with large capacities to support multiple processes or operations, processes or operations that were not contiguous to each other, engineering's requirement to interject test runs into the line, and interrupted vendor deliveries due to uncontrollable causes, i.e. weather.

In all cases where temporary kanbans are used they must be tracked. This involves understanding how much inventory is held in this kanban, how often withdrawals are made and what the reasons for the withdrawals are. Each time a temporary kanban is identified for a process, it should only be implemented if the problem is too great to solve at the current time or it is required to allow the implementation of the pull system. There must also be a focus team in place to establish a priority on these identified problems. The team must insure that a permanent solution is put in place according to the priority that has been established. Again this is not the ideal situation. The objective should always be to pursue eliminating any temporary kanban or controlled buffer that has been put in place to get around a problem. To insure this happens the problem has to be assigned to someone and they should be measured on their success.

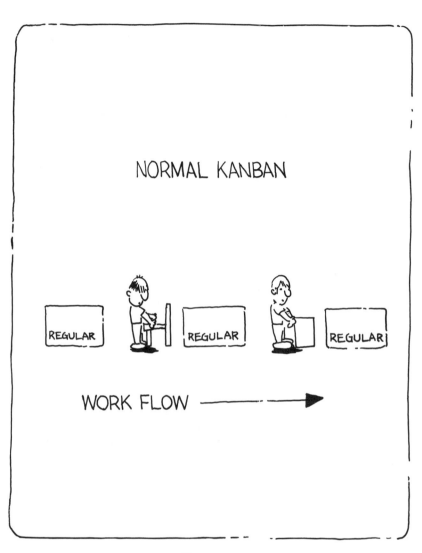

Fig. 10.2

Process Flow Improvement

The CFM approach to Process Improvement is that:

- *The work content in each process or operation should be comparable to allow a continuous flow of the product.*
- *The rate of production should equal the rate of consumption.*
- *Any process or operation that does not add value is waste and should be eliminated. For example:*
  - *— Transportation*
  - *— Counting, Issuing, Retrieving*
  - *— Storage/Buffer*
  - *— Inspection*
  - *— Rework, Etc.*
  When waste is identified, an action plan should be put in place to eliminate these non-value add processes or operations.
- *Focus is put on the utilization of the human resource. The utilization of machines is not a major factor. Machines and equipment are depreciated over time and eventually they are free except for the space they occupy and maintenance cost they incur. Human resource, on the other hand, continues to get more expensive, salaries and benefits continue to increase and investments are continually made in people through education and training.*

NOTE: Some processes and operations that are identified as waste or non-value add cannot be eliminated immediately. Technology, cost, etc. may be impediments. However, these areas should be made as efficient as possible, using the CFM philosophy, and maintaining the objective of eliminating these non-value add areas as soon as possible. One of the things IBM did to demonstrate the inefficiency of some of our manufacturing process was to calculate the Manufacturing Cycle Efficiency (MCE).

$$\text{MCE} = \frac{\text{Hands on Cycle Time}}{\text{Total Cycle Time}}$$

Cycle Time is the duration of time from the beginning of work on the first unit of the lot to the completion of the last unit of the lot.

Hands on Cycle Time is the duration of time that the product is actually being worked on (value added). Some of the manufacturing cycle efficiencies were found to be running low compared to similar processes that were using CFM philosophy.

One of the best examples of commonly accepted waste is test. In a card assembly process the test area will be from two to four times as large as the assembly area itself. There is a significant amount of money spent on new methods of testing for defects after they have already been manufactured into the product. Only a tiny fraction of this amount seems to be spent on prevention to up-grade our processes and the use of Mistake Proof Assembly. This would prevent the defects, and after continual effort, reduce the need for investment in test equipment, space, and other costly investments.

If test were to be eliminated without first eliminating the cause of defects, all of the manufacturing processes that require test would be shut down. Therefore, until we are able to eliminate the defects from the manufacturing process, test will have to remain. If test is to temporarily remain, it should be looked upon as a process and the CFM philosophy applied to it, with the intent of making test as efficient as possible. A focus should remain on test with the objective of eliminating individual testing operations when possible, with the ultimate objective of eliminating all test. If test can't be eliminated, there is no reason it can't be consolidated to make the testing process more efficient. At all times, the information generated in test must be used to improve the manufacturing process, defect prevention and product design. There are many other examples of non-value add operations and processes which can't be eliminated at this time. A program of prevention, followed by a "whittling down" process is recommended.

One of our major CFM goals is to reduce lot size, hence reducing all the waste associated with inventory and quality problems. As lot size reductions are simulated with a fixed daily going rate, the Simulation program will eventually hit a "pinch point" due to transportation time between processes or operations. First it must be understood that the improvement of transportation time and the improvement of transportation methods are not the same. The best way to improve transportation is to eliminate it. Transportation, by definition, is waste and should be tolerated only if it cannot be eliminated. In CFM a basic philosophy dictates that a product should not be moved more than an arms length through the manufacturing processes with a goal of lot sizes no greater than one. Parts should go directly to the line from the receiving docks, not to a stockroom. Suppliers should ship parts in the containers and increments used on the line, which allows us to avoid counting and other stockroom waste. The best case would have the beginning of the line connected to the receiving dock. This suggests improving the layout, which means that Operations within a Process should be an arms length away. This step should be taken before considering the purchase of expensive automated transportation equipment. Automating transportation before improving the layout could mean waste of Capital Budget.

Improving the layout also means that operators should have access to the machines with minimum walking distance. This kind of layout will be conducive to allowing operators to handle multiple operations. Experience has shown that when operators are close to different kinds of operations they will learn to run those operations without encouragement from management. When designing an area with this objective in mind, if the people are aware of management's objective of cross training, they will be even more motivated to learn new operations. This is especially true when they are not measured on amount of output. There has been much concern in recent years about providing meaningful and enriched employment. Certainly IBM's experience indicates that cross training, with a resulting variety in the job is a move in the right direction. This can only be achieved by not continuing to measure operators based on units produced.

When designing a new layout, the goal is to have parts storage within arms reach of their respective operations. If new machines are being purchased or designed for a new layout it is desirable that they should be small and mobile. This will allow you to easily reposition the machine as your Process Flowline inevitably shrinks.

U-Line Layout

The cost of human resource can be reduced by cross training, resulting in horizontal machine handling. In horizontal machine handling, one employee can handle more than one machine. They can unload and load one machine while others are running. A U-SHAPE LINE like the one in Fig (10.3 below) is an example of a layout for machines that would require a minimum number of employees.

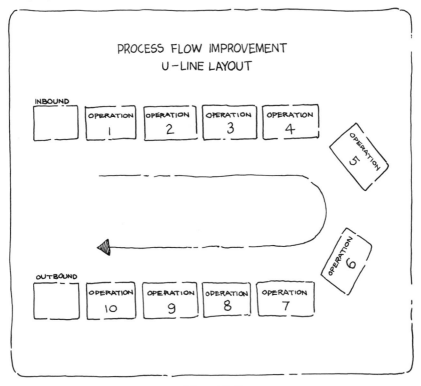

Fig. 10.3

This kind of layout is good for accommodating the CFM rule of always producing the daily going rate. If operators are trained on multiple machines, they can be reassigned as schedules decline and more people added when workload goes up.

Longitudinal machine handling requires the employees to move with the process flow from operation to operation. This is often the key to solving tough line balancing problems, to be discussed later. When the one man, one machine concept is utilized, the operators spend a certain percent of their time just watching the machine, which is a waste.

When people are not measured on the amount of output, operators are more likely to assist each other in the operation of their machines and help each other in solving problems. This was achieved with a great deal of success on a ferrite head line and a wafer process line in two IBM Manufacturing plants.

Leveling Production

Improving the process flow of product also requires leveling the production schedule. This means the production schedule has to be stable for the production period. Production lot sizes cannot be determined by the product order size; it is to be determined by Line Analysis. Customer order quantities should be assembled in the shipping areas, and the order quantity should have no direct impact on production lot size. This is accomplished by developing a weekly schedule from the monthly demands and reconciling that with the available capacity on the line. From the weekly schedules, the daily going rates are created, and parts are allocated based on this daily going rate. (The ideal situation would be to make every part number required on a daily basis). The disbursement of parts should be driven by empty kanban squares, kanban cards, or empty kanban containers. Production must be driven by the CFM rules. All processes must produce at an equal rate and the movement between processes must coincide. This means that when one is made, one is moved (or whatever the optimum lot size presently may be). Every process must receive product at the rate it consumes it, the quantity at each process or operation has to be leveled for maximum success. Takt time (time between completion of each unit, rhythm of the line or pace of parts by operation or process) must be calculated. Every operation, support discipline and operator must do whatever is necessary to make sure the Takt time is maintained (this assumes defect free products are being produced).

An example of a Take Time Calculation for one processing step.

$$
\begin{array}{rl}
\text{8 hrs. times 60 min./hr.} = & 480 \text{ minutes} \\
\text{minus two breaks} = & 30 \text{ minutes} \\
\text{net} & 450 \text{ minutes} \\
\text{Total available time} & 450 \text{ minutes} \\
\text{Daily Going Rate is} & 400 \text{ units} \\
\text{450 min divided by 400 units} = & 1.12 \text{ minutes per unit}
\end{array}
$$

Takt Time is 1.12 minutes per unit

Essentially, Takt time is the total required capacity of the operation, process, or plant in minutes per unit. *The objective that the Line must produce at a rate equal to Takt time.*

Lot size must also be determined, and is one of the results from the Line Analysis. However, as setup time is reduced and operations are moved closer together lot sizes should approach an optimum quantity (one in most cases), and processes or operations with the lowest capacity must be improved. High capacity processes or operations must produce only what is needed when it is needed on a daily basis. This could mean they are slowed down or only run intermittently, which is made possible by cross training. Whatever the daily going rate is, the discipline has to be established to make sure that this is achieved daily. In an effort to balance these operations, the time for each operation has to be known. The operation with the lowest capacity, or longest cycle time is the bottleneck. Nothing can leave the line any faster than the slowest operation or process will allow. If this operation will not support the takt time, it must be considered a bottleneck and must be improved. The bottleneck will be removed using the operation improvement, and/or setup time reduction methods etc. as determined by line analysis. The key is to understand what is causing the operation to have a long cycle time and attack the problem. It may be necessary to move some portion of the work in this operation or process to other operations in order to get the necessary balance.

After removing the bottlenecks, the next priority should be placed on the process or operation with the shortest cycle time. In some cases these operations can be eliminated by redistributing their work to other operations or processes. If these objectives cannot be met, the process or operation with the shortest cycle time may have to be slowed down, or run only intermittently. In any case, the objective is to balance the line, and produce what is needed only when it is needed. If the line still cannot be balanced enough to accommodate optimum lot size, there is another approach: the longitudinal handling approach. (see fig. 10.4 below)

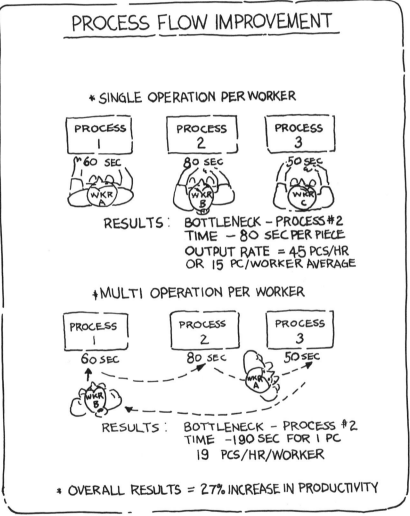

Fig. 10.4: Longitudinal Handling

In the example above there are three processes or operations, operation 1 taking 60 sec., operation 2 taking 80 sec. and operation 3 taking 50 sec. with an operator at each operation and it is not possible to balance the line any closer. The result is one piece every 80 sec., because operation 2 is the slowest operation. This gives on output of 45 pieces every hour or 15 pieces per hour per operator.

Since the line cannot be balanced, Longitudinal handling is appropriate. Two operators will be trained to operate all three operations. These two operators will be time shared among the three operations. Start operator A on operation 1. When Operator A is 20 seconds into Operation 2, start operator B on operation 1. These operators continue to follow each other. This results in a cycle time of 190 sec. for one piece, however, the output is 19 pieces per operator per hour for a total of 38 pieces per hour. This is 27% over the first example where there was one operator captive at each operation or process. The last example, of having the operators cross-trained to perform all of the operations, allows flexibility of removing operators from the line when the demand goes down and adding them back in when the demand goes up.

Note: If this process requires 39 pieces/hour or more, more than one of these processes may need to be established or overtime may be required. The maximum output using this approach in the above example is 19 pieces per worker per hour (total of 38 pieces).

Each operation within the process must be analyzed for improvement (note: do not try to analyze the entire process as an operation, processes are made up of operations and it is these operations that must be analyzed individually).

Proceed as you did in the chapter 5, entitled Operations Improvement, first eliminating the wasteful portion of the operation. To do this the content of an operation is separated into two categories, essential and auxiliary. The essential part of an operation is the value add portion. For example: actual machining, insertion of modules, deposition of patterns on silicon wafers, etc. The auxiliary part of the operation is the assisting or non-value add portion of the operation. Examples: clamping, unclamping, transportation, inspection, storage (transportation, inspection and storage of tools, fixtures and parts).

Once the essential and auxiliary categories have been identified the CFM team will begin by analyzing the operation which has a high auxiliary percentage. This can be determined from the line analysis output. Then each operation within the selected process is separated into essential and auxiliary categories, and the auxiliary categories receive the focus. The CFM team will evaluate if it is possible to perform the auxiliary part while the essential portion is being performed. Examples of techniques that will help eliminate or improve the auxiliary portion are: have parts and tools convenient on a check table so that the operator does not have to shut the operation down to gather these items. Package material so that the operator does not have to handle it excessively and waste time. Evaluate the movements of the best operator and determine how this may help other operators. Videotaping, (with operators prior consent), is a good technique. Place emphasis on houskeeping by designing the workplace so that it has a convenient place for everything and insure everything is kept in its place.

The author once observed the inefficiency caused by lack of housekeeping by a garage mechanic. He had the walls of his garage covered with peg board, and on the peg board he had hooks for his tools. Each hook had an outline in white paint of the tool that was supposed to hang from that hook. However, when he finished with a tool he would just toss it onto the work bench without bothering to return it to its proper place. As a result when he went for a tool he would have to search around in the pile of tools on his bench, wasting time, instead of being able to go to the designated location and quickly retrieve what he needed. He had designed a place for his tools, but when he didn't return them to the place he had designed, he wasted time looking for them.

When equipment is kept clean it is easier to detect problems before they become a major line stop. Shavings around a bearing or pulley, if normally clean could, indicate a bearing or bushing going bad and could be replaced before it became a major problem. A slight oil leak in a location that is normally clean could indicate a potential major problem. One of my first work assignments was operating an offset printing press. When an oil leak was detected someone would provide a very nice stainless steel oil pan to catch the oil. At least once a shift a maintenance person would come around and empty the oil reservoirs into which these catch pans drained.

Then someone would come around and fill up the reservoir that held the new oil. If the source of the leaks had been repaired when detected, considerable indirect labor could have been saved. The whole cycle of emptying the used oil reservoirs, and filling the machine with new oil was waste. Also if the repairs were made sooner major machine down time could have been avoided.

To improve the essential portion of the operation, evaluate all aspects of it. A simple procedure can be applied here, which is the 4W 1H procedure:

- *What's the Object of the operation?*
- *Who is the Subject of the operation?*
- *How are you Proceeding?*
- *Where to Place the product?*
- *When and What length of time it takes.*

A good way to analyze an operation is by videotaping, with the operators knowledge and consent. The operators should be included in the process of analyzing the videotapes. They will have suggestions for improving the operation. No one knows more about a particular operation than the person that has been assigned to it for a period of time. All operations should have work instructions that are clear, concise and with a date of release. They should include photographs and accompanying text which defines every step in the operation, including materials, tools, machines, etc., and the cycle time of the operation. The Line Supervisor should be responsible for insuring that updates are documented as improvements are implemented, and that the procedure in the work instructions being followed. Updates will be reflected by management and employee involvement in CFM.

Another important consideration in operation improvement is to keep machine resource separate from human resource. Machines and equipment are depreciated over time and eventually they are free except for the space they occupy and maintenance cost they incur. Human resource, on the other hand, continues to get more expensive, salaries and benefits continue to increase and investments are continually made in people through education and training.

The implementation team should also focus on the reduction of direct hours in an operation by analyzing the methodology used by the worker in operating the machine. This can be accomplished by studying videotapes of the operation, and arranging products and tools neatly and keeping them close at hand.

Automation

The function of the machines can be analyzed with respect to making improvements that require less human involvement. This can be accomplished by the mechanization of human motion which is automation for efficiency. If human resource required for an operation is not reduced after automation, then it is automation for show, and is a waste. Automation should be implemented in six stages:

1. *Make the process as efficient as possible with all operations performed manually.*
2. *Employ automated machines, but retain manual feeding.*
3. *Employ automated machines with automated feeding, but with manual error detection, and manual removal of product.*
4. *Use machines with automated feeding, processing, and removal, but with manual error detection and solution.*
5. *Use machines with automated feeding, processing, removal, and detection, but with manual solution of errors.*
6. *Employ fully automated machines, include sensors and feedback loops to automatically correct errors.*

Once you are committed to automation of an operation based on sound waste analysis, stage 6 must be relentlessly pursued. Most of the dollars are spent on the first three stages, but human and material waste potential still exist. Moving to stage 6 requires primarily manufacturing engineering intelligence, but removes the risk of waste.

Setup Reduction

Setup is the downtime between the last good product of one run and the first good product of the next run. CFM is dependent on our ability to produce products in small lot sizes. Economical small lot production in turn is dependent on the ability to execute setup changes in a minimum amount of time, as determined by line analysis. It was found that one of the main ingredients to determining the lot size before CFM was how long it took to make a set up. With the implementation of the setup reduction concept of CFM, lot sizes were significantly reduced. This directly reduced cycle time, increased the flexibility of the manufacturing line and increased production, which created more capacity and contributed to our objective of being the low cost producer.

The first step in rapid setup is to check housekeeping in the immediate area of the operation where the set up is being performed. This will generally expose problems associated with material and tool flow. It will also point out how important it is for everyone to know the area. These are all extremely important for rapid setups and the continuous flow of product.

The next step is to document the current method used in making the setup, showing how material should be presented and the role of each piece of equipment. The best way to do this documentation is to video tape the set up as it is being performed. An example is the Indianapolis 500 mile motor car race. The cars racing around the track are analogous to the operation. The cars must make pit stops for gas, tires, adjustments and repairs; this is the set up. A lot of races are won and lost as a result of the pit crew (the operators making the setup) being faster and more efficient than other pit crews supporting the competition. Pit crews video tape their races and practice sessions. They, along with the driver and mechanics, review these tapes (CFM implementation team). They point out new ideas for improving the way they perform when the car comes into the pits for service. They evaluate the steps crew members take, determine unnecessary motion, identify opportunity for improving tools and devices that will save time in changing tires, filling the gas tanks, and making engine adjustments, They make improvements, video tape again, analyze, and make more improvements. During all this the crew team (operators) is practicing for continued improvement in the time it takes to provide the service the race car needs so that race car is interrupted the minimum amount of time in the race (operations).

If you use video tapes or written documents when you analyze the process, focus first on the operation whose setup was identified as a pinch point by line analysis, then attack the largest time segment. When analyzing the setup, separate it into two time segments, external and internal. The external time will include those things that can be done while the equipment is still running.

- *Having tools and fixtures at machines.*
- *Having set up documentation at operations.*
- *Having roller platforms in place.*

Operators were found shutting their machine down for a setup, then going for tools and fixtures while the machine sat idle. The internal time includes those things that can only be done while the machine is shut down.

- *Exchanging drills on board hole driller.*
- *Changing chemicals in a tank.*
- *Hooking up a tester.*
- *Changing plates on a printing press.*

The external time elements were eliminated by performing these tasks while the machine was in operation. Operators would gather the required tools and fixtures, paperwork, and whatever else was necessary in making the next setup, while the machine was running. While the operator prepares for the next setup, a nearby operator may tend both of their operations.

The next step is to improve the methodology of performing the internal portion of the setup, as described in the example of the pit crew. Time and motion studies were done to determine where time was being lost. Improved fixtures were provided to eliminate lifting and to improve efficiency of exchanges. Operators then practiced their setups. If adjustments were required, they were eliminated by installing fixed stops, positioning pins and preadjusted nests.

By using the methods just explained setup times have been significantly reduced in processes where CFM has been implemented. In one case, a copier assembly process reduced the setup time by 80%. This was accomplished by video taping the setup procedure and the implementation team attacking the internal and external parts of the set up while analyzing the tape. In another plant, machine down time was reduced by 95% and labor time by 91%.

Defect Prevention

To prevent defects, the attitude has to be established that *defects can be and will be prevented 100% of the time.* The traditional quality control method, i.e., inspection after the fact, cannot achieve this objective. Statistical sampling inspection is a tool to minimize the cost of inspection. The fundamental flaw in traditional sampling inspection is that it does nothing to prevent defects, it just attempts to find them, that defects are inevitable, as was described in the chapter on defect prevention.

The initial approach taken was to improve the feedback mechanism to the affected production area. The idea was that faster communication would reduce the amount of scrap. There were processes in which defects could have been created weeks prior. There was no way of tracking it back except by going through mounds of paper. It was clear that if the feedback mechanism could be improved, a lot of defects as well as waste generated through documentation could be eliminated! The operations causing the defects must be identified and analyzed, which is the key to the feedback mechanism. Permanent prevention meant that the defect would not reoccur.

Two types of inspection were implemented: successive checks and self inspection. In both cases, inspection was moved from Quality Control to the operators. With successive checks, the operator of the subsequent operation inspects the results from the previous operation before working on the product. The operator passes it back for repair if a defect is found. This type of source inspection becomes more effective as the lot size becomes smaller and the operations are moved closer together. It also moves inspection much closer to the potential source of defects than is possible with traditional QC Inspection. Feedback is almost immediate. With the adoption of this system, defects declined to about 10-20 percent of the previous level.

Self inspection, judged superior to successive inspection by IBM, is where each operator is responsible for the results of their own operation. For this to be successful, measuring people on the number of pieces produced must be de-emphasized. In CFM training an exercise is run where the attendees manufacture a simple product using the traditional methods, focusing on productivity and using quality control inspectors. Then the attendees switch over to a pull/kanban system and we use the self inspection discipline. They are not to be concerned about productivity, to just focus on building good product and keep the line moving at a continuous pace, fixing problems as they occur. As a result the quality is almost always 100% defect free. Even though the pace has slowed down significantly the productivity is increased by at least 80%. This is because people are not going to take the time to check their quality closely if they are being measured heavily on numbers of pieces produced. The CFM measurement systems thus reduces errors, but it doesn't eliminate them. Workers are going to overlook errors sometimes, no matter who is performing the operation. The question is, how can we prevent errors from becoming defects? In traveling from site to site, and looking at the different processes and comparing those that are common, the same defects occur on similar lines throughout the company. In going back in history, it has been found that these same types of defects have been occurring for years.

Like everyone else IBM had been trying to solve these problems with quality control inspectors, operator training, operator appraisals and counseling. With the exception of quality control inspection all these things are absolutely necessary to running an efficient operation. However, the objective has to be to find the source of the defects and determine what is required to eliminate the cause so that the defects do not re-occur. Statistics provide only pointers, and control charts are meaningless if no corrective action is taken as a result. In some processes, operators counted and logged product in and out of each operation to be able to track down who was causing the defects. Less emphasis was paid to what was causing defects. Piles of data were accumulated, which seldom contributed enough toward solving the problem to justify its creation. All it accomplished was apprizing the workers on their performance, and determined which department should receive the charges for the scrap or missing product. This had to be replaced by an atmosphere of continuous improvement. The source of the defect had to be found and a permanent fix had to be implemented that would prevent the defect from reoccurring. Workers and technicians had to be trained to observe causes or problems, and the causes had to be eliminated. This required the reduction of process variances:

- *Dimension instability and positioning accuracy of machines.*
- *Tools had to be more accurate, homogeneity of tool stock and standardization of build methods.*

- *Accurate reproduction of set-up conditions and adjustments.*
- *Procedure of standardization and attention to detail.*

Since it is impossible for someone to be 100% accurate at all times, Mistake Proof Assembly methods and design for manufacture had to be implemented. Parts are being designed so that they fit only one way, look alike parts are being colored coded. Some operators are able to tell when something is not right just by the sound of the machine, and they in turn train others. Containers are being designed that will prevent workers from picking parts from the wrong bins. A few years ago a problem was found with product getting to the field without all the documentation being packaged with the product. People were trained, and they were counseled; the usual procedure when encountering this type of a problem. Things improved for awhile, but then returned to being a problem after a short time. A Mistake Proof idea was implemented by putting light sensors on the documentation bins. This required the operators to break the light beam on each bin when reaching for the documentation before the process would move on. This eliminated the problem and no more complaints were received from the field.

In one facility a large tester with an oscilloscope screen required an engineer to replace the light bulb when it burned out. The engineer attended a CFM class. He told the class that sometimes he had a difficult time explaining to his wife why he was called out at three o'clock in the morning to change a light bulb. When CFM was implemented into this process the operators were trained to change the bulb. Soon, the operators were able to predict a range of time when the bulb would burn out and it could be replaced at a more convenient time, instead of waiting for it to burn out. Before the burn out occurred the screen would gradually get dimmer and this was the signal to change the bulb. This is another example of how operator involvement actually resulted in a preventive, anticipative solution that the engineer could not have easily developed.

Statistical process control should be used to insure processes operate within predefined tolerances. This effort is part of the continuous improvement effort. SPC can allow operators to quickly detect out-of tolerance situations, and often prevent production defects. This will predict time intervals when processes will go out of tolerance

150

and alert operators to potential or real out of tolerance conditions. Light or sound signals can be used when occurrences are infrequent and error is correctable. The line should automatically stop when occurrences are frequent and/or error is not correctable. At one IBM location, a set of lights was installed; green, yellow and red, similar to the ones described in Japan. The Japanese companies installed these lights at each operation. When the green light is on the line is running smoothly. If the yellow light comes on the operator has alerted everyone to a potential out of tolerance condition. However, if the red light comes on the line stops, and because of the lights being at each work station, the support people knew which operation had the problem. In the IBM facility one set of lights had been installed in a location where everyone could see them. However, you couldn't tell which operation had the problem when the line stopped. The operator had to go to the technician and bring him to the operation with the problem. A lot of time was wasted because a shortcut was tried.

Other examples of Mistake Proof methods are devices that detect the correct shape through contact/non-contact. Operation movements can be traced to check whether they were executed the required number of times, and in the correct sequence. The conclusion is that defects can be prevented 100% of the time, that self checking operations are good and self stopping operations are better; self correcting operations are the best of all.

Getting Started

The first step in CFM implementation is obtaining top management support for the program. This is absolutely essential as total success cannot be achieved without this support. The second step in the implementation of CFM is to establish a CFM team. Initially the team should consist of three full time people: a team leader (strong 2nd level manufacturing manager), a Manufacturing Engineer, and a knowledgeable manufacturing technician. The team leader should be extremely knowledgeable of the manufacturing process. They will begin by focusing on line analysis. As more work is done the team is expanded to contain more people such as: 1st line manufacturing managers, technicians, specialists, key operators, manufacturing engineers (for process and tooling), equipment engineers, maintenance, industrial engineers, quality engineers, production control, design and development engineers and software system support personnel. They can help in the development of Mistake Proof Assembly methods and Design for Manufacture methods. The larger number of people exposed to CFM training, the better the result. The expanded portion of the CFM team will focus on a more comprehensive line analysis, generate bench mark models, and help to design kanbans. Kanbans are defined as the maximum amount of product allowed at the input and output stations of an operation that will allow that operation to support the daily going rate. The CFM team is responsible for:

- *Developing a master schedule and budget for management review.*
- *Reporting on progress versus schedule.*
- *Assuring that necessary CFM training occurs.*
- *Developing detailed working schedules which supports the master schedule.*
- *Develop CFM personnel performance measurements which are consistent with the company's beliefs.*
- *Develop support requirements from other areas, such as Data Processing, Purchasing, etc.*
- *Establish a "CFM Room" which is HQ for the CFM team, so people can ask questions and review ideas.*

In summary, the CFM team is responsible for making it happen. The team will report to the Manager of Manufacturing. Three examples of successes we have achieved in IBM are shown in the tables below:

Results of the implementation of CFM into our Super Pilot Lines.

Memory Wafers

- *Cycle Time improved by 79%*
- *WIP reduced by 64%*
- *Cost reduced over previous plan by 20%*
- *Space Savings 10%*
- *Manpower Savings:*
  Manufacturing 30%
  Manufacturing Engineering 15%
  Maintenance 25%

Personal Computer Cards

- *Output per employee increased* *10%*
- *Quality improved* *30%*
- *Inventory Turns increased* *50%*
- *Manufacturing Cycle Time reduced* *50%*
- *Cost of Value Add was reduced by* *19%*

Storage Products

- *Reduction of WIP* *47%*
- *Manufacturing/Test Engineering*
  Hold Centers reduced *70%*
- *Cycle Time reduced* *50%*
- *Rework (on line screed) reduced* *47%*

Implementation of CFM principles and concepts has required strong management commitment from the top and the involvement of all functions: manufacturing, engineering (ME, IE, DEV., ETC.), purchasing, production control, materials destribution maintenance, marketing and other support groups. IBM established implementation teams made up of strong team leaders from manufacturing management, with representatives from all support disciplines as required and technical direction from a staff of CFM experts from one of our group headquarter staffs. IBM implementation teams are insuring that CFM education is provided to everyone involved: manufacturing managers, operators, technicians and support groups. IBM is creating an environment that produces communication and cooperation among all disciplines. Decisions and action taken are produced and owned by all team members directed toward the pursuit of: Getting all the people involved, eliminating all waste and achieving total quality control. IBM's objective is to achieve the lowest possible cost, defect free products.

CHAPTER 11

PEOPLE INVOLVEMENT

Introduction:

In making the transition to Continuous Flow Manufacturing, it is important to recognize that many traditional beliefs must be modified. Examples include:

- *Defect prevention using new tools, such as Mistake Proof Operations*
- *Small Lot Production instead of large lot production*

Beliefs cannot be conquered by force, but only by persuasion. Lincoln was criticized for being too gentle with conquered Confederates. He replied that he knew of no better way of conquering an enemy than by making him a friend. The same wisdom applies to any transition which requires the active assistance of many people. Persuasion will promote cooperation, force will promote confrontation.

Without question, persuasion grows from knowledge, not ignorance. The goals and methods of CFM are logical and acceptable. Thus if we do an adequate job of training and education, the path will be far smoother. As is true of any change, there is a natural fear as to "what will it do to me?" We must recognize and deal with this concern.

Education

Education in CFM principles must be broad based to be effective. It should include not only Manufacturing Engineering, but R&D, Quality Control, and Foremen and Key Operators. To show why all these functions should be involved, consider a few examples.

One company, which is renowned as a leader in JIT, failed to get R&D involved. The engineers thought it was "just an inventory reduction program." Because of this lack of knowledge, no Mistake

Proof Operations were developed in the first two years. This problem has now been remedied, and Manufacturing has identified over 100 Mistake Proof Operation projects based on actual defects. Nevertheless, a high defect rate and cost persisted because of lack of engineering involvement.

Another example was apparent in the IBM chapter. You will recall that the first attempt at Line Analysis simulation failed because the input data did not accurately describe the actual line. In this case, people from the line immediately found the error.

Education must not only be broad in its reach, it must be deep enough to comprehend all CFM tools. In the majority of American implementations, only a fraction of the tools are being used. People implement the Pull System and Process Flow Improvement and say "we're doing JIT." In most of these cases, Rapid Setup and Defect Prevention are not thoroughly addressed. Line Analysis is even less often employed. By making a wide range of employees aware of all these tools, those of high initiative will seize the opportunity. Further, all personnel will have a common language for discussing problems.

As is true of any endeavor, there is a "critical mass" needed to keep the improvement effort going. As an example, one company trained five engineers, and implemented the first stages of the Toyota system. Within a year, two of the engineers were transferred, and the program was slowed. Education must also proceed at Executive levels so that top management support can be attained.

Dealing With Change

But what do we do with the manufacturing overhead personnel who have been manning waste functions in the hidden factory? No one knows your business like your employees, and expanding sales is going to require a lot of knowledge. The areas of the business in which personnel growth is healthy are those that contribute to increased sales, more product diversity and lower manufacturing cost. Thus we must be alert to find individuals who can fill roles in marketing and sales, development engineering, and manufacturing engineering. All three areas, properly managed, have a leverage effect of cash benefits to the company much greater than the salary outlay. Additional education may be necessary to properly fit the individual to the task, but education is a lot cheaper than the results of ignorance. The expansion of sales will open up new Direct Labor jobs for the Overhead personnel who are not otherwise qualified.

We want to find a new and more rewarding career opportunity in the productive factory for each person who manned the hidden factory.

Our ultimate goal is to increase sales at a faster rate than we increase people. This will assure high profits, job security, and better products for the customer.

Conclusion

We end as we began.

. . . There is, in fact, no limit to the benefits which human beings may bestow upon one another by the highest exertion of their diligence and skill.

Our view of the future is of a world of freedom and plenty, with exciting and rewarding work in proportion to each person's intelligence and energy. The waste which limits our ability to bestow benefits upon one another can be eliminated. We believe the Continuous Flow Manufacturing system is but a small start which can be expanded to even more important spheres of thought and action.

APPENDIX I

RAPID SETUP & OPERATION IMPROVEMENT

The goal of simultaneously obtaining low cost and product flexibility is clearly dependent on economically building small lots of defect free product. But how do we actually achieve this goal?

In the Appendix we will discuss the economical production of small lots. This goal can and has been achieved as the result of design and manufacturing engineering methods which you can adopt. There is nothing cultural about them.

In the first chapter, we explained that Henry Ford's opposition to any product variation was based on the need to avoid the "inevitably" long setup time. Thus one of our goals is to reduce setup time to a negligible value. If we can achieve this goal, we can employ Continuous Flow Manufacturing to build a variety of products and avoid the waste of Batch Production. Thus we can simultaneously achieve product variety and low cost. Coupled with Defect Prevention methods, the goal of lowest cost production can be continuously approached.

In the formula for Economic Lot Size, a negligible setup cost will yield a small Lot size, yet one which is economical to build. An impressive example of rapid setup is the setup of the 2700 ton press at the Zama plant of Nissan which stamps out door frames. The setup of such a large press typically takes 6 hours. Nissan now manages the setup in 6 minutes. This has allowed a 95% reduction in Lot size. Nissan expects to reduce the setup time to 45 seconds, which is the Takt Time of the plant. If they can achieve this goal, they will need an inventory of only four door frames! Rapid setup allows the plant to meet the unpredictable and changing customer demand quickly and without the hidden inventory cost. In this chapter we will describe the details of the Four Step Rapid Setup Method.

The Four Step Method applies to all setups, including chemical, process, assembly as well as machine tools. We will give some examples from all these applications to illustrate the power of the method.

157

The Four Step Method also applies to the reduction of Operation Time, the time required to actually build a unit.

Rapid Setup

Rapid Setup methods were first developed by Toyota, and primarily applied to the setup of machine tools. As we mentioned above, the methods are applicable to the setup of any Operation, be it chemical, process, or a machine. The majority of setup tasks in a factory are relatively simple, and the necessary reductions are achieved by housekeeping and organization. Some tasks, such as machine tool setup, can be challenging. We shall tackle some of the tough tasks for illustration, but the reader should understand that these are in the minority.

Let us first agree on a definition of setup time:

Setup Time is the time between the last defect free product of one lot to the first defect free product of the next lot.

Note that the actual time to setup the Operation is a portion of the setup time. The time to gather tools, materials, and all other factors while the Operation is shut down are also contained in the above definition.

Analysis of Setup

The setup of any equipment or process can be analyzed and broken down into four steps:

1. Preparation: All the Materials and tools for the next setup are brought to the work station. The tools are tested to make sure that they work; and there are no shortages. The previously used tooling and material is removed, cleaned, and returned to storage.

2. Setup: The new tooling and material is mounted at the work station.

3. Measurements, Settings, Calibrations: Positioning tools verifying that material is in tolerance, that the proper force, pressure, termperature required by the process is present.

4. Trial Runs, Adjustments: A test run is made to verify accuracy of calibrations in the previous step, and that the product conforms to requirement.

Each of these steps is subject to enormous time reduction. As with all Manufacturing Engineering (ME) activities, a determined effort with a lot of intelligence and a small amount of money will achieve miracles of Setup Time reduction.

The Four Step Method of Rapid Setup

1. Separating Internal from External Setup: "Internal" setup is that portion which can only be done with the process shut down. "External" setup can be done while the process is running.
2. Converting Internal to External Setup.
3. Streamlining Internal Setup.
4. Make settings quantitatively using guages, and eliminating adjustments.

We will now discuss each of these steps with a few examples.

1. *Separate Internal from External Setup:* Often when performing a setup, a machine or process is first shut down, and then people go to look for material and tooling. This is frequently due to the fact that a machine operator watches the machine work, or drinks coffee, rather than getting tooling ready for the next setup. Don't get mad unless the workers were trained to prepare the next setup. It is essential to apply analysis to separate what can be done before the machine or process is shut down. We refer to this as the external portion of the setup. It is the job of the line supervisor, assisted by ME and the Operator to develop and document a set of work instructions to do the preparation for external setup. If many items of tooling are required, often a "Check Table," a plywood board with the outline of each tool, can be helpful. The worker should verify that the material needed for the next lot is available or being made ready in time for the next run.

   Typically, this process of organizing, and training workers

159

to do setup can cut the setup time by 30-50%. The external setup of the next Lot can be initiated as soon as the processing of the present lot begins. Instead of a worker watching the machine, he can proceed with the next setup. This first step was primarily organization, things that should have been done all along and generally are not done. The "cost" of preparing for the next setup is usually merely training the worker to prepare the next setup rather than watch the machine or process run.

2. *Converting Internal to External Setup:* Many setup steps seem to require that the machine or process must be shut down. Examples include changing drill bits, blades, changing PC board width on a wave solder machine, heating a die or vat, pulling a vacuum on an injection mold, adjusting a die height, etc. Modifications to your existing equipment at modest cost will often allow the conversion of one of the "inherently" internal setups to an external setup. this external setup can then be performed while the machine or process is working, and hence no longer affects lot size.

A few examples will illustrate the point:

• *Thread Dyeing:* In dyeing thread, the thread is held on a rack immersed in a vat. The vat is then heated with steam. With this method it takes a long time to reach and hold the correct temperature, and the color quality is not always good. During this one hour heating period, the process was shut down.

The "heating of the vat" was transformed from internal to external setup by setting up a second vat which as being preheated while the first vat was dyeing. In addition, a second thread rack was installed so that, while dyeing was proceeding, the worker would prepare a second rack. Thus loading thread also became an external setup. The total setup time was thus reduced to 5 minutes.

• *Vacuum Molding:* This process requires the near complete evacuation of air from the mold before resin is injected, or else a poor quality product will result. Approximately two minutes is spent pumping, during which time no injection can occur. Since the process is shut down, pumping is defined as "internal setup."

The process of pumping down the mold was converted from internal to external setup by installing a secondary vacuum tank with a volume of 1000 times the mold capacity. The secondary vacuum tank is already evacuated. By connecting it to the mold cavity by a valve, it is evacuated in 10 seconds, rather than 2 minutes, with proportional gains throughout.

• *Continuous Material:* Spools of material are frequently used, e.g., in the manufacture of springs, transformers, etc. In changing from one material to another, one must shut down the de-reeler drive, lift out the old material, lift in the new, and re-attach and re-tension the drive. During this 20 minute change, the machine is, of course, shut down. By adding a second spool, and attaching the beginning of the new spool to the end of the old, the shut down due to setup is eliminated. Again, spool changing was converted from internal to external setup. Only re-tensioning and run-in is required, a 1 minute setup.

These examples show that, in addition to reducing the lost labor of setup time, one can also drastically reduce the Operation time of the process, increasing productivity and production capacity.

3. *Streamlining Internal Setup:* After all ingenuity has been exhausted in converting internal to external setup, we must make the internal setup as efficient as possible.

Very often, a change in setup requires changing of tools, brackets, collars, vats, etc. These items are sometimes built in to the machine or process by the original manufacturer, and are held in place by bolts. Often the change requires a re-alignment of the machine or process. The manufacturer of the equipment may not have had rapid setup in mind. We must take the initiative to make the Internal Setup as efficient as possible. The two primary techniques for achieving this goal are by Common Setup, and Quick Functional Clamps.

Common Setup: The idea is to provide a single mechanism which performs several setups.
For example:
• *Profiling Templates:* A copying lathe uses a template to cut a copy, much as the locksmith copies keys. To change

templates in a large lathe requires great skill, precision, and repeated adjustments to properly align and position the template. It typically takes a good machinist 30 minutes until the first good part of the new run is produced.

The lathe was modified to accept an axle in the template position. Four different templates were precisely positioned and welded to the axle. Templates could be changed in less than a minute rotating the shaft to the desired template. No adjustments were needed because the axle was precisely and permanently aligned to the lathe.

• *Change of Die in a Press:* In changing from one die to another, one must make adjustment for the differing die heights. This adjustment is generally perofrmed by a highly skilled operator while the press is shut down. However, if shims are welded to the bottom of each die so that the heights are all identical, the height adjustment is no longer required. To align the die in the press, we included centering pins, which were mounted to centering holes. An adjustment must usually be made due to the differing thickness of material. This affects the "shut height" of the press. The adjustment can be eliminated by automatically gauging the thickness and correcting shut height with a programmable controller.

One must still bolt the die to the press. By welding shims to the clamp space, one obtains a uniform height from the top of clamp surface to the press on all dies. This will allow the use of a quick functional clamp to be discussed in the next section. A 3 hour step became 3 minutes with proportional reductions in inventory and floorspace.

• *Quick Functional Clamps:* If a bolt has 10 threads, one does not secure the two pieces until the 10th turn, i.e., the first 9 turns are "wasted." Thus if we could develop an attachment method which only needed the last turn or two, we would reduce setup time. This is particularly important if the setup requires several bolts or clamps.

• *Pear Shaped Hole:* Consists of a hole large enough to pass the bolt head, and a slot sized for the bolt shaft. A single turn tightens the bolt over the slot, a single turn loosens, sliding the bolt to the large hold to unmate the parts.

162

• *Cams, Toggle Clamps, Split Bolts* are examples of one touch clamps, since moving the handle exerts or removes great clamping force. Split thread bolts are excellent for larger force. The thread has three 60 degree slots removed from the thread of both the male and female. This allows one to drop the male in and tighten with a 60 degree turn, the strength can be made as great as you wish by increasing the length of the bolt shaft and hence the number of threads. The conclusion we reach is that every setup connection should be redesigned to use a one-turn or one-touch functional clamp. By this means, setups that took hours can be performed in minutes.

Some Setups require forces which cannot be achieved by the above methods. Such an example is the exchange of die in a 2700 ton press previously mentioned. The principles of Rapid Setup still apply! One of the authors visited the Zama plant of Nissan. The 2700 ton press had 6 die and was stamping out door frames. Each die is attached to the ram with four huge bolts. Each bolt shaft is driven by a pneumatic motor. When the exchange is made, the motors loosen the bolts. The bolts are slid away from the die. The whole die, punch and platform ride on rails. This assembly is rolled away and is replaced by the new die, punch and platform. The bolts are inserted, the die slid, and the motors tighten the ram to the new die. Pressing begins anew. The exchange of all 6 die now takes 6 minutes, and die are changed four to six times per day, depending on the models being run of the line. The immediate goal is to reduce Setup time to 3 minutes. The ultimate goal is 45 seconds. Why 45 seconds? Because that is the rate of car production (Takt Time) at Zama. By reducing Setup time to 45 seconds, an inventory of only one car is required.

4. *Elimination of Adjustments:* One of the most time consuming problems with setups is the post setup trial run and adjustments. Can we eliminate adjustments? Is that possible? First we must draw the important distinction between a setting made during setup, and adjustments made later based on trial runs.

The first step toward eliminating adjustment is to replace intuition and experience with measurements, be they mechanical or digital. This frequently involves permanently welding a dial gauge, digital meter, or other scale to the machine.

The need for trial runs and adjustments is frequently occasioned because there is nothing to measure. For example, it is necessary to align the center of the milling machine to the center of the material being cut. This is typically done by making a cut, measuring, adjusting, etc. The problem is occasioned because the center line of the milling machine is an imaginary line. By installing rails on the machine parallel to the table's center-line which are locked, it becomes unnecessary to align the cutter to the piece. Time consuming adjustments were thus eliminated as was potential scrap. By rendering the imaginary center line visible, and setting to that center line via the rails, adjustments were eliminated.

Application of Rapid Setup to Electronic Assembly: Typically, a variety of different assemblies are built at a single work station. In Batch production, the setup change from one electrical module to another seldom receives much Manufacturing Engineering attention. Usually, a day is consumed in gathering parts, tools, chasing shortages and finding the necessary jigs and fixtures. With large batches, the Operation is often clogged with material. We will assume that the assemblies have some parts in common, and some different. The Work Station should be designed to have permanent bins for a few days usage of common parts, and replaceable bins for the unique parts. Recall the discussion of Chapter 4 in regard to Takt Time and Computer Kanban. The production demand on each workstation is derived from the explosion of the Final Assembly Bill of Material. The sub-assembly information is sent to Raw Materials stores for kitting and delivery. The material is pulled before need, and acts as an input Kanban to the Operation. Kitted parts are thus released when needed. If the transport time from stores to the Operation is lengthy, Buffer Kanban kits should be stored at the Operation. The quantity should equal the Delay

Time divided by the Takt Time. Our goal is, of course, to eliminate the waste of transportation and related time. The setup procedure should be documented and practiced. When kitting in small lots, setup time is significantly reduced. Reductions from 8 hour to 30 minutes are achievable. An all day setup can typically be reduced to 30 minutes.

We have now discussed and provided examples of the Four Steps of Rapid Setup. The purpose of this account of Rapid Setup was to give you the confidence that setup time can be made negligible, eliminating the need for large lots.

The Line Analysis program previously described will give you several excellent candidates for Rapid Setup efforts in the proper priority. Adequate Manufacturing Engineering efforts must be focused on target, and that target must be faced with *"bulldog determination that knows no defeat."*

Machine Modification

In many of the Rapid Setup examples, we spoke of modifying expensive capital equipment to facilitate rapid setup. It might be argued that, by such modification, the machine loses its resale value. Even assuming this is true, remember: The machine was bought to serve, not rule the company. If it must be modified to properly serve, it should be modified. After all, you are a Manufacturing company, not a Machine Sales company. The alternative is inefficient large batch production, with all its attendant evils.

As was discussed in the chapter on continuous flow, old equipment should not be automatically scrapped for the newest, biggest and fastest. Just as continuous flow causes us to avoid single Super-Machines in favor of smaller units, old equipment may meet the special purpose needs cheaply. Again, the comparison between Nissan and Toyota is instructive. Nissan is having a hard time competing with Toyota, and appears to be losing market share and profit. In discussing the causes with two leading Japanese consultants, they both agreed that over investment in fancy equipment, robots, and automation was Nissan's problem. Toyota gets more output out of old equipment with faster setups. Toyota is referred to as a "stingy" company.

It has been estimated that the Japanese spend 60% of their Capital Equipment Budget on the modification of existing equipment, whereas U.S. companies spend 80% on new equipment.

Operation Improvement

Each Operation of a Process represents a work station where man and machine meet to add value to the product. We have two goals in our drive to eliminate waste:

- *To eliminate all efforts that do not add value. We call these Auxiliary Functions.*
- *To increase labor and capital efficiency of the value add portion, which we will call the Essential Functions.*

Again, Line Analysis will give us the priority of operations which need improvement. The Operations Improvement effort is very much like Rapid Setup: the names change but the method does not. The methods are:

Four Steps of Operation Improvement
1. *Separate Auxiliary functions*
2. *Eliminate or streamline auxiliary function*
3. *Improve the Essential function*
4. *Design for Manufacture*

The Auxiliary portion can be performed while the machine is working. The Essential portion is that which adds value, i.e., cutting, inserting, etc.

1. *Separation of Auxiliary from Essential:* To take a smiple example, let's assume that the Operation consists of a Numerically Controlled Milling Machine that is drilling and countersinking a large plate. The Essential portion is the actual drilling and countersinking of the holes. The Auxiliary includes finding the material, cleaning, transporting, inspecting, etc.

2. *Eliminating Auxiliary:* Our goal is to perform all Auxiliary functions while the Essential function is proceeding. In this way, the Auxiliary function has been effectively eliminated. By having the material within an arms reach, a large but un-

noticed source of waste can be eliminated i.e., wandering around looking for material. This waste is particularly prevalent with Batch production because of large lots and poor housekeeping.

The cleaning and transporting should also be done while milling is proceeding. All Auxiliary functions must be completed within the period of time taken by the Essential function. In this way, the Auxiliary function has been effectively eliminated, since it no longer affects Operation time. In the milling example you may have to speed up cleaning by using an ultrasonic system, speed up inspection using a "Go-No Go" jig, etc. As we improve the Essential function, we must also continue eliminating the Auxiliary so that it can be completed within the Essential time.

Conversion of Essential to Auxiliary:

The "Downtime" of the operation can be further reduced if, in the Rapid Setup effort, a second plate was available on which to clamp material while the machine is milling. The cleaning and transporting should also be done while milling is proceeding. Thus the downtime due to clamping is largely eliminated, because this effort has been converted from Essential to Auxiliary.

3. *Streamlining:* You may be able to speed up the machining by classical Methods Engineering techniques. For example, you may use carbide bits instead of high speed steel, use a coolant, program in a quick tool rotation to speed up drilling but avoiding overheating, etc. All the Auxiliary functions also need to be eliminated or streamlined so that they can be finished in the Takt time. In this example, we may want a fast solvent or ultrasonic cleaning to be considered, a template to eliminate inspection, etc. Video taping (with prior worker's consent) can be a very valuable method of detecting and eliminating time waste. The worker can often be of great help in analyzing the tapes. The classical Methods Engineering and Ergonomic Methods are of great help.[1]

4. *Design for Manufacture:* If the Operation time is still too long to keep up with the Takt Time, you could consider a faster machine. This should be a last resort as it is expensive

and generally inflexible, even though it is often cost effective.

Before we automate, let's exhaust all possibilities of manual methods, then look at the product itself. Do we really have to countersink these holes? If not, we could drill two plates at once. Although we'd rather have a lot size of one unit, in this case over production is not the problem. Do we even need the holes? Could we use snap-on fasteners?

[1]Krick, E. "Methods Engineering," New York: Wiley 1966.

APPENDIX II

STATISTICAL PROCESS CONTROL
AND CAPABILITY IMPROVEMENT

Statistical Process Control (SPC) is a powerful tool for process control and for capability improvement. The basics of SPC have been well known since the 1930's. For a thorough modern description of their use in manufacturing, see *Introduction to Statistical Quality Control*, by Douglas C. Montgomery, John Wiley and Sons, New York, 1985. We are going to give a brief overview of how SPC works.

Fig. 9.1A shows a graph of measurement made on a part dimension at various points in time. Perhaps this is a result of 100 percent inspection. A graphical display of data such as this is called a *run chart*. The upper and lower specification limits (USL and LSL) are also shown on the graph. Notice that during this time period, no defective parts are produced, but that by the end of the period a downward drift in part dimension has occurred. If this were allowed to continue, defective parts would eventually be produced.

Statistical process control operates by taking small samples from the process at relatively frequent intervals and plotting relevant information on a control chart. This is illustrated in Fig. I.1(b)(c). The types of control charts shown in I.1(b)(c) are the x and R control charts. The x control chart is plotting the average dimension of five units selected from the process, and the R chart is plotting the range of the dimensions in those five units (the range is simply the difference between the largest and smallest measurement in the sample). Both control charts have a set of statistically derived upper and lower control limits (UCL and LCL). These control limits warn when the variation in the process has become so large that the results cannot be explained by chance, and so some management action must be undertaken to investigate and correct the process. That is, when points plot inside the control limits the process is said to be 'in control' and when points exceed the control limits the process is said

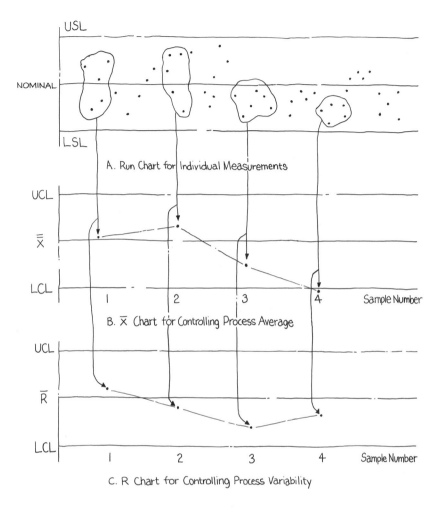

USL

NOMINAL

LSL

A. Run Chart for Individual Measurements

UCL

$\overline{\overline{X}}$

LCL

| 1 | 2 | 3 | 4 | Sample Number |

B. $\overline{X}$ Chart for Controlling Process Average

UCL

$\overline{R}$

LCL

| 1 | 2 | 3 | 4 | Sample Number |

C. R Chart for Controlling Process Variability

Fig. I.1: Run Chart, $\overline{X}$ – Chart, and R Chart

to be 'out of control.' An out of control process must be investigated, corrected and eventually improved. Notice that the x chart detects the downward drift in the dimension of the part by the time the fourth sample has been selected. The range chart does not indicate an out of control condition, implying that the scatter or variability within a sample has remained relatively consistent.

The manufacturing engineer or operator gets much useful information from the control chart. In this case, the control chart has indicated that it is the process average that is out of control, not the sample variability. Sometimes, a particular pattern of points will appear on the chart, and the information in this pattern may have diagnostic value to the engineer or operator. We can then use the information in this pattern to improve the process, thereby reducing its variability, and lowering the likelihood that a defective unit will be produced.

Control charts can be used to detect shifts or 'upsets' in a process, as this example indicates. However, their real power is in providing information which allows management and engineering to improve the process. Systematic use of control charts coupled with an active group of engineers, managers, and operators who use the control chart information to look for improvement opportunities will always lead to a process with improved capability.

Where can statistical process control methods be used most effectively? In practice, they can be used anywhere, although they are most powerful in process, fabrication and machine intensive processes. SPC consists of more than control charts. It provides a consistent set of tools which are useful in tracking down an unknown source of defects. Other SPC tools that are useful in a Defect Prevention program include:

1. ***Pareto Analysis:*** This is just a graph of total defects by defect type. Usually, we find that most of the defects are attributable to a few defect types (Pareto's law). To illustrate, assume that a sub-assembly, such as a PC board, has a variety of defects. Table I shows the frequence of occurrence and cost. Figure I.2 is the pareto diagram on defect types. We note that the most important problems are related to wave solder.

2. ***Fishbone Diagram:*** Given that we have a wave solder problem, a team is formed including the wave solder technician, line supervisor and Industrial Engineer. Together, they identify the possible causes of the defects. A convenient way to display the potential sources of defects is shown in Fig. I.3. The diagram looks like a fish skeleton and hence is called a 'Fishbone Diagram.' Notice that in the major block called 'solder process,' there are five major process variables which may affect defects. These five variables may form the basis for a designed experiment to reduce solder defects.

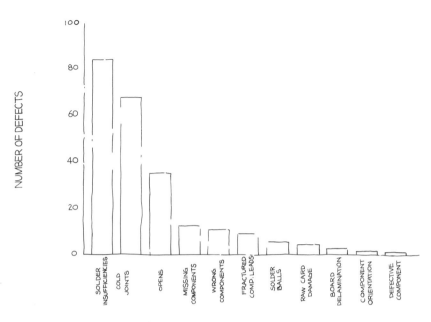

Fig. I.2: Pareto Analysis of Defects in Printed Circuit Boards

3. *Defect Concentration Analysis:* This is just a picture of the product showing the areas containing the defects. Analysis may disclose a physical reason for this concentration of defects.

Statistical Process Control can always be used to track and potentially control the variability and defects from any Operation. SPC will give indications as to the source of defects. If the defect is Operator related, it may be possible to develop a Mistake Proof Operation method which will 100% prevent the defect. If not, SPC can be continued to prevent any unusual problems. If the defect is related to a process, SPC will provide valuable insight into the selection of variables for a Designed Experiment.

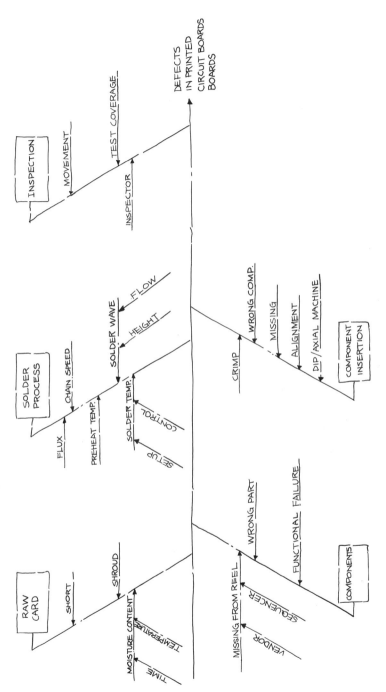

Fig. I.3: Cause-and-Effect (Fishbone) Diagram

173

GLOSSARY OF TERMS

Batch Production: The production control method whereby product is built in lots determined by present and anticipated needs, or as determined by the Economic Lot Size formula, and in all cases determined by what is needed to overcome hidden and/or visible problems. (See also Push System.)

B.A.U.: Business as usual ("Batch Production")

Continuous Flow Manufacturing: An ongoing process requiring an optimally balanced line to achieve the lowest cost, defect free product.

Control Chart: A statistical chart used to reveal the deviations from control values. The two most common charts are the plot of average values (X) and the plot of the range of values (R).

Cycle Time: The total time to complete a production work on a lot of units. If the lot size is 100 units, the cycle time is the time needed to complete all 100 units. The factory cycle time is the time from order placement to delivery.

Daily Going Rate: The daily demand for product based on firm customer orders, or established production schedule which rate has been leveled as far as possible. (See Level Production.)

Defect Prevention: The body of techniques used to prevent defects or produce a 100% defect free product, rather than remove them solely by inspection and test. The techniques include Mistake Proof Assembly, Self Checking Machines, Successive Checks, Design for Manufacture, Statistical Process Control and Design Experiments.

Designed Experiments: The technique of reducing the variability in the output of a process. Defining those parameters which may affect a product specification, and conducting a set of experiments which will optimise the desired result versus variation of parameters.

Economic Lot Size Formula: The formula which determines the economic lot size as the point at which interest cost of the lot balances the setup cost.

Specifically:

$$\text{ELS Quantity} = \sqrt{\frac{2(\text{Setup Cost}) \, (\text{Useage})}{(\text{Interest Rate}) \, (\text{Unit Cost})}}$$

The formula does not include the Hidden Inventory Costs.

External Setup: That portion of the setup which can be performed while the Operation is producing product or in operation.

E.C. or E.C.O.: Engineering change. Defined as a product design change generally introduced after the product is in production.

Fishbone Diagram: A branching diagram which shows the connections between defects and the causes.

Flow Rate: The rate at which each unit of production is completed, the inverse of the Takt time, in units per minute.

Hidden Inventory Costs: The costs which are usually absorbed into Manufacturing Overhead and not explicitly known. They include the cost of storing, counting, moving, inspection, scrap, reworking, inventory.

Industrial Engineer: An engineer devoted to the reduction of cost and defects of products.

Internal Setup: That portion of the setup which can only be performed when the Operation is not producing product or in operation total minutes available in a day.

Inventory Turns: A measure of the relative efficiency in a production system. Defined as the Cost of Goods Sold divided by average inventory.

Just In Time: See Continuous Flow Manufacturing.

Kanban Information: A card, designated space or container holding a designated quantity of product establishing a disciplined quantity of product passing from one process or operation to another.

Kanban: A physical container, marked floor area, or other device which holds a quantity of material equal to the pre-determined lot size.

Lead Time: The total time required to perform a task. It may include order time, delivery, receiving, inspection, waiting time, production, transport, etc.

Level Production: The scheduling process of attempting to spread customer orders over a period of time such that the production rate is nearly constant.

Line Analysis: A simulation method which allows the determination of potential problems versus a desired change in production. Line Analysis can be performed with a manual simulation of the MFG process or with a software program.

Line Balancing: Designating the work done in a Process such that each Operation has the same or nearly same Operation time.

Line Flow Diagram: A diagram showing the sequence of operations and/or processes which make up a Process (First step in doing a Line Analysis.)

Manufacturing Cycle Efficiency: A measure of the relative efficiency in a production system. Defined as the hands on time divided by the total throughput time.

Manufacturing Engineer: See Industrial Engineer.

Operation Time: The time needed to complete the work on a single unit through a single operation or process.

Operation: A single work station where one task is performed on the product.

Operations Improvement: The Four Step process of elimination of waste to reduce the time of actually building the product or sub-assembly.

Preventive Maintenance: Performance of routine maintenance on machines and equipment, on a scheduled basis, in an attempt to avoid major repairs or breakdowns.

Process Capability Improvement: The effort to drive the variability out of a process such that a higher and higher percentage falls within the acceptable product specifications. The two principal tools are Statistical Process Control and Designed Experiments.

Process Capability: The spread of values of a product's characteristics which are obtained when the process is repeated many times. The distribution of values is intrinsic to the process, and has nothing to do with the acceptable product specifications.

Process Control: The effort to maintain a process output within a given range such that the variation about the desired value is random.

Process: The total of all Operations needed to complete a sub-assembly or product.

process: Work that is performed at an Operation which is not of an assembly nature. Examples of a process include machining, painting, plating, diffusion, chemical reactions, etc.

Pull System: The production control method whereby product is built or processed only as demanded by succeeding Processes. The pull system should start at the end of the process and ripple back to the beginning of the process.

Value Add: Any effort which transforms the product another step toward completion. Vaule add efforts do not include the Hidden Inventory costs of warranty costs, ie. transportation, storage, inventory/buffers, handling, queues, etc.

W.I.P.: Work in Process.

Workcenter: See Operation.

INDEX

64K Random Access Memory, 88, 118
256K Random Access Memory, 88
Accounting Systems, 119
Allied Chemical, 96
Automation, 69, 94, 145

Batch Production, 7, 27, 174
  and flexibility, 28
  and waste, 33
Bethlehem Steel Co., and Taylor, 12
Bill of Materials Processor (BOMP), 61
Boeing, 96
Britain, ROI of American Firms, 112
Buick, 14
Business as Usual, and Batch
  Production, 28
B.A.U. (see Batch Production), 174

Caldwell, Phillip, 21
Carnegie, Andrew, 119
Caterpillar Tractor, 96
Chevrolet, 17
  in decline, 23
Churchill, Winston, 21
Computer Aided Design (CAD), 95
Computer Aided Manufacture (CAM),
  95
Computer Integrated Manufacturing,
  106
Continuous Flow Manufacturing, 2, 26,
  27, 43, 174
  relation to JIT
  and Ford, 19
  education for, 154
  implementation, 122, 151
Control Chart, 174
Cross Training, 71

Cycle Time, 54, 55, 174
  and cost advantage, 59
  manufacturing, 109
Cycles of Learning, 58

Daily Going Rate, 174
Deere & Co., 100, 112
Defect Prevention, 6, 43, 44, 147, 174
Deming, W. E., 40, 78
Depression, 25
Design for Manufacture, 87, 167
Design of Experiments, 90, 174
  and residuals, 90
  often neglected, 45
Digital Equipment, 95
Dupont, 23, 96

Eastman Kodak, 96
Economic Lot Size Formula, 6, 33, 174
Economic Order Quantity (see
  Economic Lot Size)
Engineering Change Order, 76, 116
External Setup, 175
Exxon, 96
E.C. or E.C.O., 175

Fishbone Diagram, 171, 175
Flexible Manufacturing Systems, 102
Flow Rate, 175
Ford, 96
Ford Taurus, 111
Ford, Henry, 5, 14, 125
  and market share, 23
  and Taylor, 14
  and Toyota, 39
  quality system, 17
Four Step Method, 42, 66, 157
Four W and One H, 144

France, ROI of American Firms, 112
Fuji-Xerox, 112

GE, 95
General Motors, 23, 24, 96, 98
Gilbreath, Frank, 12
Grant, Richard, 24
Growth Rate, 114
Grundig, 79

Hewlett-Packard, 4
    and JIT implementation, 44
    in Japan, 112
Hidden Factory, and Waste, 36
Hidden Inventory Costs, 34, 175
Honda, 115

IBM, 3, 4, 25, 26, 32, 95
    and Continuous Flow manufacturing, 125
    and self inspection, 148
    in Japan, 112
Improvement Methods, 64
    continual, 123
Industrial Engineer, 175
Inspection Fatigue, 87
Internal Setup, 175
International Harvester, 96
International Power Machines, 29
Inventory Turns, 175
Inventory Turns Ratio, 108
    and competitiveness, 4
    and Detroit, 18
    and Ford, 18
    Toyota, 19

Japan, 39
    Postwar crisis, 39
    Robot Policy, 101
    ROI of American Firms, 112
Job Shop, 32
Juran, J. M., 40
Just In Time, 1, 40, 43, 175
    and trial and error, 46
    at IBM, 127
    difficult implementation, 45

Kanban, 175
    computer and MRPII, 60
    information, 175
    system, 42
    buffer, 71
    computer, 43, 60
    temporary, 53, 133
Kuboto, 112

Lawrence, Robert, 113
Lead Time, 175
Learning Curve, 69
Leveling Production, 42, 139, 176
Line Analysis, 2, 3, 176
    and rocks chart, 46
    at IBM, 130
    comparison with languages, 45
    example, 49
Line Balancing, 72, 176
Line Flow Diagram, 176
Lockheed, 96
Longitudinal Handling, 141
Lot Sampling, 87
Lower Control Limit, 169

Magneto Ignition, 14, 16
Manufacturing Cycle Efficiency, 135, 176
Manufacturing Engineer, 176
Manufacturing Overhead, and Waste, 40
Manufacturing Strength, Seven Measures, 121
Market Share, 118
Marketing, 5, 7
MBA Graduates, 117
McDonnell Douglas, 96
Mercedes-Benz, 73, 96
Metal Inert Gas (MIG) Welding, 100
Midvale Steel Co., and Taylor, 12
Minnesota Mining & Manufacturing (3M), in Japan, 112
Mistake Proof Operation, 81, 150
    Often neglected, 45

Model T, 18, 20, 21
  and Sloan's strategy, 23
  eclipsed by Chevrolet, 24
Mostek, 88
MRPII, 6, 60
  and Kanban, 43

National Academy of Engineering, 117
Nissan, Plants, 5
Non-Repetitive Manufacturing, 60

Operation, 176
Operation Improvement, 44, 69, 166,
  176
Operation Time, 176

Pareto Analysis, 171
People Involvement, 154
  at IBM, 127
Pfizer, in Japan, 112
Phillips, 79
Porter, Michael, 124
Prevention of Defects, 81
Preventive Maintenance, 70, 176
Primary Wiring, 30
Process, 117
process, 177
Process Capability, 89, 176
Process Capability Improvement, 176
Process Control, 176
Process Flow Improvement, 44, 70, 135
Proctor & Gamble, in Japan, 113
Product Complexity, Impact on Quality
  and Cost, 75
Product Cost, 110
Product Delivery Team, 116
Production Capacity Increase, 55
Pull System, 42, 44, 177
  at IBM, 132
  Using Line Analysis, 53

Quality Circles, 92
Quality Control, New Focus, 86
Quality of Conformance, 73

Quality of Design, 73
Quality, Cost of, 79

R Chart, 169
Rapid Setup, 6, 21, 44, 65, 145, 157
  Often neglected, 45
Return on Investment, 118
Return on Sales, 119
Ricoh, and Benchmarking, 111
Robotics, 69, 94, 98
Roosevelt, Theodore, 105
Research and Development, 5, 7
  and Watson, 25

Scientific Management, 11
Seasonality, 61
Secondary Wiring, 30
Self Checking Machines, 84
Semiconductor, 8, 26
Semiconductor Industry, 87
Setup, External, 160
Setup, Internal, 159
Shell Oil Co., 96
Skinner, Wickham, 31
Sloan, Alfred, 17, 23, 25
Sony, Plants, 5
Statistical Process Control, 89, 169
Successive Checks, 16, 86
Supplier Relations, 92

Takt Time, 57, 100, 101, 139, 140
Taylor, Frederick, 11, 16, 28, 30, 65
Texas Instruments, 95
Texas Instruments, in Japan, 112
Time & Motion Study, 13
Tohatsu, 114
Total Quality Control (see Defect
  Prevention), 127, 129
Toynbee, Arnold, 123
Toyoda, Kirchiro, 39
Toyota, 42
  system in America, 41
  trial and error, 47

and Robots, 105
Kamigo, 9, 5
Transport Time, 70

U Shaped Lines, 71, 138
Uninterruptible Power Supplies, 29
Union Carbide, 96
Upper Control Limit, 169
U.S. Steel, 119

Value Add, 177
Video Cassette Recorder (VCR), 74
Videotapes, Usefulness in Rapid Setup, 146
Volkswagen, 73

Waste, Elimination, 129
and Ford, 20
Watson, Thomas J., 25
Wilson, Woodrow, 14
Workcenter, 177
W.I.P., 177

$\bar{X}$ Chart, 169
Xerox, 96
10 Series Copier, 116
and Benchmarking, 111

Yanmar, 112

Zama Plant of Nissan, 157
Zeppelins, and Ford System, 29